THE NATION'S REPORT CARD **naep**

The Science Report Card
Elements of Risk and Recovery

Trends and Achievement Based on the 1986 National Assessment

Ina V. S. Mullis □ Lynn B. Jenkins

With an Overview Based on
Contributions and Comments from the Interpretive Panel:

Richard Berry □ Audrey Champagne □ John Penick
Senta Raizen □ Iris Weiss □ Wayne Welch

EDUCATIONAL TESTING SERVICE

 ETS®

September 1988

P
507
mullis

gift · A. Cleghorn 3/20/90

CONTENTS

Interpretive Overview
Science Learning Matters   4

PART I

Tilting the Balance?
Trends in Science Proficiency 19

Chapter 1
The Road to Recovery
Trends in Average Science Proficiency for
the Nation and Demographic Subgroups 23

Chapter 2
What Students Know About Science
Levels of Science Proficiency
for the Nation and Demographic Subgroups. 36

PART II

Turning the Tide of Neglect?
The School Context for Science Learning. 63

Chapter 3
The Opportunity to Study Science
Exposure to Science Instruction 66

Chapter 4
The Impact of School Science
The Relationship Between Course-taking
and Proficiency in Science Content Areas 79

Chapter 5
The Nature of School Science
Teacher Qualifications and Classroom Practices 91

PART III

The Unscientific Americans?
Experiential, Home, and Attitudinal
Factors Associated with Science Learning 103

Chapter 6
Using the Tools of Science
Independent Experiences in Science Learning 105

Chapter 7
Home Support for Science Learning
Parental Involvement and Educational Support 117

Chapter 8
How Students Perceive Science
Student Views on the Utility
and Value of Science Learning 123

Procedural Appendix 134

Data Appendix 146

Acknowledgments 150

INTERPRETIVE
OVERVIEW

Science Learning Matters

Science Empowers and Enriches

The distinctive character of our own time lies in the vast and constantly increasing part which is played by natural knowledge. Not only is our daily life shaped by it, not only does the prosperity of millions . . . depend upon it, but our whole theory of life has long been influenced, consciously or unconsciously, by the general conceptions of the universe, which have been forced upon us by physical science.

—Thomas Henry Huxley, 1880

UXLEY'S STATEMENT on the value of science is even more valid today than when it was written more than one hundred years ago. Then, and increasingly so now, the pervasive influence of science on the quality of our lives makes an understanding of science central to our personal, national, and global welfare. With the accelerating pace of scientific discoveries and technological advances over the last century, knowledge of the methods and products of science has become ever more essential to full participation in contemporary American society. In addition to enhancing the minds and lives of individual citizens, science learning is crucial to the social and economic development of our country. To understand and resolve the increasing number of societal problems related to science and technology—for example, the depletion or pollution of natural resources—our schools must produce a large majority of graduates who are literate about these issues and an increasing percentage of students who are both highly prepared and motivated for advanced careers in science.

From a broader perspective, there is growing concern over our country's future ability to compete in the global economy.[1] A highly technological nation such as ours requires civic and educational leaders whose understanding of science and technology is sufficient to make decisions based on valid information and rational analysis. Our nation's economic growth and its place in world markets are determined in part by its ability to provide intelligent leadership in technological fields.

The State of Science Learning

It is widely believed that the condition of science education in this country needs improvement, and the results of NAEP's 1986 science assessment do not assuage this concern. In 1983, the National Science Board's Commission on Precollege Education in Mathematics, Science, and Technology described the implications of neglecting science education:

> Alarming numbers of young Americans are ill-equipped to work in, contribute to, profit from and enjoy our increasingly technological society. Far too many emerge from the nation's elementary and secondary schools with an inadequate grounding in mathematics, science and technology. As a result, they lack sufficient knowledge to acquire the training, skills and understanding that are needed today and will be even more critically needed in the 21st century.[2]

Since this statement was made, as many as 100 national reports have been issued calling for greater rigor in science education and suggesting numerous reforms. The nation has responded by updating standards for school science programs, strengthening teacher preparation, increasing the use of assessments, stiffening graduation requirements, and implementing a wide variety of research efforts to deepen our understanding of science teaching and learning. Despite these efforts, average science proficiency across the grades remains distressingly low.

Trends for 9-, 13-, and 17-year-olds across five national science assessments conducted by NAEP from 1969 to 1986 reveal a pattern of initial declines followed by subsequent recovery at all three age groups. To date, however, the recoveries have not matched the declines.

---

[1]Education Commission of the States' Task Force on Education for Economic Growth, *Action for Excellence: A Comprehensive Plan to Improve Our Nation's Schools* (Denver, CO: Education Commission of the States, 1983).

[2]National Science Board Commission on Precollege Education in Mathematics, Science, and Technology, *Educating Americans for the 21st Century* (Washington, DC: National Science Foundation, 1983).

- **At age 17, students' science achievement remains well below that of 1969.** Steady declines occurred throughout the 1970s, followed by an upturn in performance between 1982 and 1986.

- At ages 9 and 13, the declines were less sizable than those at age 17 and recovery began earlier, in the late 1970s. In 1986, however, **average achievement at age 13 remained below that of 1970 and at age 9, simply returned to where it was in the first assessment.**

National expectations are high. Students are expected to complete their high-school studies with sufficient science understanding for assuming their responsibilities as voters and as efficient contributors in the workplace. In addition, school science is expected to prepare adequately for postsecondary science courses those students who are continuing their formal education. Unfortunately, these expectations have not been met. An examination of NAEP trends in science proficiency suggests that a majority of 17-year-olds are poorly equipped for informed citizenship and productive performance in the workplace, let alone postsecondary studies in science.

> ... NAEP ... suggests that a majority of 17-year-olds are poorly equipped for informed citizenship and productive performance in the workplace, let alone postsecondary studies in science.

- More than half of the nation's 17-year-olds appear to be inadequately prepared either to perform competently jobs that require technical skills or to benefit substantially from specialized on-the-job training. The thinking skills and science knowledge possessed by these high-school students also seem to be inadequate for informed participation in the nation's civic affairs.

- Only 7 percent of the nation's 17-year-olds have the prerequisite knowledge and skills thought to be needed to perform well in college-level science courses. Since high-school science proficiency is a good predictor of whether or not a young person will elect to pursue post-secondary studies in science, the probability that many more students will embark on future careers in science is very low.

These NAEP findings are reinforced by results from the second international science assessment, which revealed that students from the United States—particularly students completing high school—are among the lowest achievers of all participating countries.[3]

- At grade 5, the U.S. ranked in the middle in science achievement relative to 14 other participating countries.

- At grade 9, U.S. students ranked next to last.

- In the upper grades of secondary school, "advanced science students" in the U.S. ranked last in Biology and performed behind students from most countries in Chemistry and Physics.

---

[3]International Association for the Evaluation of Educational Achievement, *Science Achievement in 17 Countries: A Preliminary Report* (New York, NY: Teachers College, Columbia University, 1988).

Given evidence from both the NAEP and international results that our students' deficits increase across the grades, projections for the future do not appear to be bright. The further students progress in school, the greater the discrepancies in their performance relative both to students in other countries and to expectations within this country. Because elementary science instruction tends to be weak, many students—especially those in less affluent schools—are inadequately prepared for middle-school science. The failure they experience in middle school may convince these young people that they are incapable of learning science, thus contributing to the low enrollments observed in high-school science courses. Unless conditions in the nation's schools change radically, it is unlikely that today's 9- and 13-year-olds will perform much better as the 17-year-olds of tomorrow.

The Status of Science Learning for "At-Risk" Populations

Students do not all arrive at the kindergarten door with equal opportunities and aspirations. Social and economic realities have begun to have an impact long before that time, and schooling does not serve to eradicate these inequities.

The NAEP data show substantial disparities in science proficiency between groups defined by race/ethnicity and gender.

■ Despite recent gains, the average proficiency of 13- and 17-year-old Black and Hispanic students remains at least four years behind that of their White peers.

■ Only about 15 percent of the Black and Hispanic 17-year-olds assessed in 1986 demonstrated the ability to analyze scientific procedures and data, compared to nearly one-half of the White students at this age.

■ While average science proficiency for 9-year-old boys and girls was approximately the same—except in the physical sciences—a performance gap was evident at age 13 and increased by age 17 in most science content areas. At age 17, roughly one-half of the males but only one-third of the females demonstrated the ability to analyze scientific procedures and data.

■ The marked edge in the physical sciences shown by boys at grade 3 increased at grades 7 and 11; by the eleventh grade, the performance gap in physics was extremely large.

■ The large difference in science performance by gender cannot be explained by differential course-taking patterns; in some cases, the proficiency gap between high-school-aged males and females actually increased with course-taking.

7

Since a higher proportion of Black and Hispanic children than White children come from homes of lower socioeconomic status, disparities in performance attributed to race/ethnicity may be due in large part to differences in such factors as parents' education levels and access to reading and reference materials in the home. In fact, recent research on mathematics achievement shows that when other school and home factors are controlled, students' socioeconomic status accounts for a large part of the performance gap.[4] Economically disadvantaged students are likely to enter school at an educational disadvantage, because they appear to be behind their peers and are therefore placed in remedial classes. The consequence of this early tracking is that many of these students are poorly prepared to pursue higher-level science and mathematics coursework when they get to high school.[5]

In the case of performance disparities between male and female students, there is growing evidence of differential treatment and opportunities in science instruction. Teachers have higher expectations for boys than girls, and ask them higher-level questions.[6] Textbooks may also send the message that most of the notable accomplishments in science are attributable to White males. Because there are still relatively few female and minority scientists, students are unlikely to encounter them as role models.

Teachers have higher expectations for boys than girls, and ask them higher-level questions.

While one would expect in-school experiences to contribute to students' participation and achievement in science, the NAEP data also suggest that some of the factors underlying performance differences may originate outside of the school. This appears to be particularly true for the performance gap by gender. In the 1986 assessment, females were substantially less likely than males to report science-related activities or experiences.

. . . females were substantially less likely than males to report science-related activities or experiences.

While the NAEP data cannot tell us what causes these differences, there is evidence from other sources that sex- and race-role stereotyping are often major deterrents to the participation of female and minority students in science and science-related activities.[7] For example, parents, peers, the media, teachers, counselors, and curriculum materials may give females and minority students the idea that only certain roles are appropriate for them. Within- and out-of-school experiences appear to reinforce one another in creating and perpetuating differences in achievement.

---

[4]Donald Rock et al., *Excellence in High School Education: Cross-Sectional Study, 1972-1980* (Princeton, NJ: Educational Testing Service, 1984).

[5]Jeannie Oakes, *Keeping Track: How Schools Structure Inequality* (New Haven, CT: Yale University Press, 1985).

[6]Marsha Matyas and Jane Kahle, "Equitable Precollege Science and Mathematics: A Discrepancy Model," paper presented at the Workshop on Underrepresentation and Career Differentials of Women in Science and Engineering (Washington, DC: National Academy of Sciences, 1986).

[7]Shirley Malcom, " Why Middle School Is Important to Science Equity Concerns," in *Developing Options for Managing the National Science Foundation's Middle School Science Education Programs*, ed. Iris Weiss (Research Triangle Park, NC: Research Triangle Institute, 1986).

Research on teaching and learning indicates some approaches that appear promising for improving the participation of females and minorities in science. For example, to counteract the aversion toward physical science that girls seem to develop even before they enter school, elementary science should include an abundance of hands-on activities related to concepts in electricity, magnetism, and other areas, structured so that girls play an active rather than a passive role. In addition, appropriate role models should be provided through interactions with both male and female scientists of various racial/ethnic backgrounds, both in person and through textbooks, films, and other instructional materials.

Teacher education, both pre-service and in-service, should make teachers aware of the more subtle behaviors that communicate low expectations to particular students . . .

Teacher education, both pre-service and in-service, should make teachers aware of the more subtle behaviors that communicate low expectations to particular students, and give them assistance in implementing instructional techniques that are effective with female and minority students, as well as White males. Finally, alternative mechanisms need to be developed to foster the skills that will prepare students for academic sequences in high school rather than curtail their opportunities.

Opportunity to Learn Science

Two distinct aspects of an opportunity to learn are the amount of time spent on instruction and the quality of that time. The first is a necessary but insufficient condition for the second; however, results from the 1986 NAEP science assessment suggest that *neither* condition of the opportunity to learn science is afforded our nation's youth.

- More than two-thirds of the third-grade teachers responding to NAEP's 1986 teacher questionnaire reported spending 2 hours or less each week on science instruction; many spent more than that amount of time maintaining order and disciplining students in the classroom.

- Eleven percent of the third graders assessed in 1986 reported having no science instruction at the time of the assessment; in addition, one-third of the elementary students who were receiving instruction reported spending no time on science homework.

- All but 6 percent of the seventh graders reported taking some type of science course in 1986, but enrollment dropped substantially by grade 11. Only 58 percent of the eleventh-grade students were taking a science course at the time of the assessment.

- Approximately half of the teachers in grades 7 and 11 reported spending three hours or less providing science instruction each week.

- Of the seventh- and eleventh-grade students taking a science class in 1986, 12 to 16 percent reported spending no time on science homework each week.

These findings are corroborated by recent literature in which teachers reported spending only an average of 18 minutes per day on science at grades K-3 and only about 29 minutes per day at grades 4-6. Across these grades, the amount of time spent was greatest for reading, followed by mathematics, then social studies and science—a ranking which had not changed since 1977.[8] Thus, even for those students who are enrolled in science classes, the amount of time actually spent on science learning appears to be minimal.

. . . very few students in this country take advanced science courses.

In addition, very few students in this country take advanced science courses. Preliminary results of a follow-up transcript study of eleventh-grade students participating in the 1986 assessment indicate that while 90 percent of these graduating students had studied at least one year of Biology, only 45 percent had studied one year or more of Chemistry, and 20 percent that amount of Physics. Although these findings represent increases in science course-taking since 1982, enrollments generally remain low from an international perspective. Only about 6 percent of all high-school students in this country take advanced courses in Biology, compared with 45 percent of the students in Finland and 28 percent of the students in English-speaking Canada. Similarly, students studying advanced Chemistry and Physics represent a very small percentage of the total U.S. student population; by comparison, in other countries these students represent as much as one-sixth to one-fourth of the total student population.[9]

The Relationship Between Amount of Science Instruction and Proficiency

A recent report issued by the National Academy of Science Committee on Indicators of Precollege Science and Mathematics Education reviewed the research literature linking instructional time and student learning; it concluded that at both the elementary- and secondary- school levels, the amount of time given to studying a subject is correlated with student performance as measured by achievement tests. The report also found that the amount of time spent on homework is correlated with student achievement, and that teachers' attention to homework affects its contribution to performance.[10]

[8]Iris Weiss, *Report of the 1985-86 National Survey of Science and Mathematics Education* (Research Triangle Park, NC: Research Triangle Institute, 1987).

[9]International Association for the Evaluation of Educational Achievement, *Science Achievement in 17 Countries: A Preliminary Report* (New York, NY: Teachers College, Columbia University, 1988).

[10]Richard J. Murnane and Senta A. Raizen, eds., *Improving Indicators of the Quality of Science and Mathematics Education in Grades K-12* (Washington, DC: National Academy Press, 1988).

These conclusions are further reinforced by NAEP findings from the 1986 assessment, which suggest positive associations between science proficiency and the amount of time spent in science learning (i.e., through course-taking and homework), particularly among eleventh-grade students. It may be, however, that highly proficient students choose to take more courses or select more challenging courses that require more homework. Further, as previously noted, time spent in science classes *per se* cannot guarantee the quality of that instructional time. Although both common sense and empirical findings indicate that more time spent in science instruction will improve science learning—thus supporting reforms that are targeted toward reducing absenteeism, increasing science course-taking requirements, and assigning more homework—great care also must be taken to address the quality of that instructional time.

Because educational reforms implemented in the 1980s cannot be expected to have immediate impact and their full effects may not be noticeable for some time, the slight progress evidenced in the NAEP results may portend improvements for the future. It must be recognized, however, that improvements in average performance seen in the 1986 assessment were largely the result of students' increased knowledge *about* science rather than increased skills in scientific reasoning. This finding, coupled with the disappointing state of science education, suggests that current reforms tend to be aimed primarily at the symptoms rather than the disease.[11] What has traditionally been taught in science may be neither sufficient nor appropriate for the demands of the future, necessitating reforms that go beyond increasing students' exposure to science and that center on implementing new goals for improving curriculum and instruction.

Science Learning in the "Spirit of Science"

Embarking on fundamental reforms of science curriculum and instruction requires a reexamination of the conceptual underpinnings of science education. Science educators have maintained that hands-on and laboratory experiences should be an integral part of science instruction, explaining that it is appropriate for science teaching and learning to parallel the methods of investigation used by scientists to understand the natural world.[12]

Results from the 1986 science assessment do indicate a positive relationship between students' use of scientific equipment and their proficiency in the subject, particularly at the eleventh-grade level, but cause-and-effect

[11]Paul DeHart Hurd, "Perspectives for the Reform of Science Education," *Phi Delta Kappan* (January 1986).

[12]Wayne Welch, "A Science-based Approach to Science Learning," in *Research Within Reach: Science Education*, eds. David Holdzkom and Pamela Lutz (Charleston, WV: Appalachia Regional Laboratory, 1984).

11

relationships cannot be addressed by NAEP data. Schools with laboratory facilities and other scientific equipment may be the wealthier schools, populated by advantaged students who tend to perform better in academic assessments. Disciplined research is needed to substantiate the impact of hands-on activities on science proficiency, and the appropriate role of these activities in science instruction.

Findings from the NAEP assessment also suggest positive associations between participatory classroom activities and science proficiency, and between attitudes toward science and students' proficiency in the subject. Again, while the NAEP data are suggestive, they by themselves do not permit the conclusion that more participatory activities or efforts to improve students' views of science will necessarily raise achievement levels for any given student population. Decisions to strengthen science education that may be suggested by the NAEP data must be firmly based on relevant research and experience.

Given these caveats, some aspects of science practice can be used to analyze the nation's science education program and reflect on NAEP findings. What are the features of the scientific enterprise that our science education system might emulate?

Activities. Procedures of investigation—such as observation, measurement, experimentation, and communication—allow the scientist to gain an understanding of natural phenomena. In addition, mental processes such as hypothesizing, using inductive and deductive reasoning, extrapolating, synthesizing, and evaluating information are necessary to scientific investigation, as are the less well defined but no less important skills of speculation, intuition, and insight. An effective science learning system would provide students with opportunities to engage in these activities, and encourage science teachers to model them in their classrooms.

Beliefs and Assumptions. Scientists appear to operate in accordance with a set of beliefs about the natural world that guide their methods of inquiry and the knowledge yielded by these methods. For example, scientists believe a real world exists that can be understood; they assume that nature is not capricious and that events in nature have causes.

Implementing the methods of scientific inquiry yields knowledge about the natural world, contained in the form of facts, concepts, hypotheses, theories, and laws. These structures are characterized in part by scientists' beliefs, making it possible to communicate scientific knowledge, give it logical coherence, offer explanations, and make predictions. Yet another key aspect of the knowledge of science is its tentativeness: Scientists view findings not as final statements but rather as reasonable assertions about some distant, but seldom reached, truth.

12

Characteristics of Scientists. Certain personality traits seem to characterize successful scientists, and these may provide additional guidance for determining the features of an effective science education program.[13] Among the salient traits of successful scientists are curiosity, creativity, and dedication. Scientists ask questions about and are sensitive to the world around them. The critical nature of the profession requires a strong belief in one's ability to learn, and an ability to distinguish between productive and unproductive ideas. The joy of discovery is a driving force in scientists' professional lives; they are hungry for knowledge and recognition, and strive to achieve both.

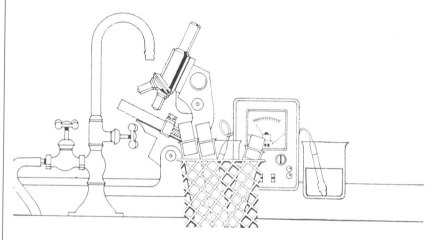

Elements of the Model in Light of NAEP Findings

The "spirit of science" model suggests that the most effective learners are those who are actively engaged in the learning process and accept responsibility for their own learning. In contrast, data from the 1986 NAEP science assessment indicate that by grade 11, almost half of the students have decided not to take any more science courses, few spend time on independent science-related hobbies or activities, and only about half think that what is learned in science class is useful in everyday life. This portrait is indeed far from the model.

The brief analysis of the scientific pursuit of learning also suggests the value of providing students with greater opportunities for observing natural phenomena both within and outside the classroom, and engaging them in measuring, experimenting with, and communicating data from the surrounding world. As active rather than passive participants in the learning process,

The critical nature of the profession requires a strong belief in one's ability to learn, and an ability to distinguish between productive and unproductive ideas.

. . . the most effective learners are those who are actively engaged in the learning process and accept responsibility for their own learning.

---

[13]W.R. Klemm, ed., *Discovery Processes in Modern Biology* (Huntington, NY: Robert Krieger Publishing Co., 1977).

students can strengthen their full range of mental processes, from formulating hypotheses, explaining observations, and interpreting data to other thinking skills used by scientists in their efforts to build understanding.

However, the NAEP data show:

- Only about one-third of the seventh graders and slightly more than half of the eleventh graders reported that they were asked to hypothesize or interpret data in their science class at least on a weekly basis.

- Only 35 percent of the seventh graders and 53 percent of the eleventh graders reported working with other students on science experiments at least on a weekly basis.

- Over half of the third graders and more than 80 percent of the seventh and eleventh graders reported *never* going on field trips with their science class.

- Sixty percent of the seventh graders and 41 percent of the eleventh graders said they *never* had to write up the results of science experiments.

- Only about 46 percent of the teachers of seventh or eleventh grade reported access to a general-purpose laboratory and only 64 percent of the eleventh-grade teachers reported access to a specialized laboratory for use in teaching science.

A classroom environment that emulates the "spirit" of science is characterized by collaboration between teachers and students to test knowledge that is gained and a willingness to modify this knowledge in light of new evidence. This setting encourages students to wonder about the world around them and actively seek to understand it. It builds their thirst for knowledge and strengthens their sense of responsibility to learn. Teachers provide role models for students and stimulate their curiosity. Yet numerous studies of the last few years—for example, John Goodlad's *A Place Called School*—have indicated that most teaching, including science teaching, is instead dreadfully dull.[14]

For the classroom to mirror the real-world practice of science, the teacher should be an active model, spending less time lecturing and more time engaging students in hands-on activities and asking open-ended questions than do teachers in general.[15] In contrast, students in the 1986 NAEP science assessment reported few opportunities to explore natural phenomena directly or engage in discussions about the limited experiences that they did have. They revealed a preponderance of class time spent listening to teachers'

> Only about 46 percent of the teachers of seventh or eleventh grade reported access to a general-purpose laboratory . . .

> For the classroom to mirror the real-world . . . the teacher should be an active model, spending less time lecturing and more time engaging students in hands-on activities and asking open-ended questions . . .

[14]John Goodlad, *A Place Called School* (New York: McGraw-Hill Book Company, 1984).

[15]Ronald J. Bonnstetter, John E. Penick, and Robert E. Yager, *Teachers in Exemplary Programs: How Do They Compare?* (Washington, DC: National Science Teachers Association, 1983).

lectures; in addition, limited information on school curriculum suggests that scientific content appears to be largely textbook- and workbook-driven, reflecting little—or not at all—the recent technological advances in the domain of science.

Science Curriculum

To provide curriculum, instruction, and facilities appropriate to the demands of science teaching and learning, it is clear that a number of substantial changes are needed. The need for greater availability of classroom laboratory facilities is undeniable. The 1985-86 National Survey of Science and Mathematics Education found that while most teachers believed that laboratory classes were more effective than non-laboratory classes, lectures were reported as their primary teaching technique. However, this paradox may be partially explained by the fact that a substantial percentage of teachers do not have access to adequate laboratories, science equipment, supplies, and other resources needed for teaching science.

Perhaps even more crucial than greater access to laboratory facilities are the more fundamental, but less obvious, changes associated with teaching and curriculum. Cross-cultural studies shed some light on the direction that is needed, revealing significant differences between science curricula in this country and those in Japan, China, East and West Germany, and the Soviet Union.[16] In these five countries, science content is more closely linked to the requirements of modern industrial society, and the instructional approach is to teach an array of disciplines over a period of years, maintaining continuity across the grades. In comparison, the prevailing practice for public school students in the United States is to take one science subject for one academic year and then move to another discipline the following year—sometimes referred to as the "layer-cake curriculum."

Before sweeping changes in curriculum are adopted, research is needed to establish the effects of the content, sequence, and amount of science instruction on students' science learning. Because education is cumulative, perhaps the best way to understand how curriculum and course-taking affect student knowledge and competence in science is to conduct longitudinal studies that follow students through at least one year of science instruction. One difficulty in conducting this type of research, beyond cost, is to describe in sufficient detail the content and other attributes of the science curriculum actually presented to students, beyond the course title and textbook used. By examining important aspects of both the intended and implemented curriculum—and relating these "opportunity to learn" data to students' mathemat-

---

[16]Margrete Klein and F. James Rutherford, eds., *Science Education in Global Perspective: Lessons from Five Countries* (American Association for the Advancement of Science: Selected Symposium Series, No. 100. Boulder, CO: Westview Press, Inc., 1985).

ics achievement—the Second International Mathematics Study offers a useful model for research in science learning.[17]

Science Instruction

In the ideal science classroom, students would have abundant opportunities to question data as well as experts, to design and conduct real experiments, and to carry their thinking beyond the information given. They would identify their own problems rather than always solving problems presented by tests, teachers, or other authoritative sources. Much of their problem-solving might also be in the form of practical experience. Through these experiences, students would come to realize that knowledge in science is tentative and human-made, that doing science involves trial and error as well as systematic approaches to problems, and that science is something they can do themselves. To provide such instruction, teachers need to be prepared with a keen understanding of the nature of science, rather than just its requisite facts. Like their students, few teachers have had opportunities to conduct real experiments under real conditions; therefore, as a starting point, teacher education should provide opportunities for prospective science teachers to work with students at a variety of grade levels and in a variety of settings. The traditional one-semester methods course required of prospective teachers should give way to two or three semesters of coursework in this area, using video and audio tapes, intense feedback from professionals, and methods instructors who model the types of instruction desired.

At the same time, courses in the history, philosophy, sociology, and applications of science should be required of pre-service science teachers, enabling them to develop a rationale for teaching science that integrates their goals for teaching science and what is known about effective teaching practices, the nature of science, and the ways in which children learn—as well as methods of evaluation that are compatible with all of these. Teachers with such a rationale are prepared to be flexible and can integrate research into classroom practice. These teachers approach teaching scientifically and provide models of active inquiry for students. Perhaps teachers with such rationales would rely less on textbooks and would find them more useful as reference materials than as curriculum guides. As a result, students may come to see that science class is a place where the role of student and teacher alike is to raise questions and investigate possible answers and to explore new techniques and methodologies.

Teachers with a new rationale for science instruction would not only be competent and consistent, but also concerned with domains beyond knowledge—including the role of career choice, creativity, attitudes, thinking,

In the ideal science classroom, students would have abundant opportunties to question data as well as experts, to design and conduct real experiments, and to carry their thinking beyond the information given.

. . . few teachers have had opportunities to conduct real experiments under real conditions . . .

At the same time, courses in the history, philosophy, sociology, and applications of science should be required of pre-service science teachers . . .

---

[17]Curtis C. McKnight et al., *The Underachieving Curriculum: Assessing U.S. School Mathematics from an International Perspective* (Champaign, IL: Stipes Publishing Co., 1987).

application, and communication in science instruction. Students successful in these domains would more closely approach the levels of science literacy called for by virtually all educators concerned with the current state of science education.

Conclusion

Evidence from NAEP and other sources indicates that both the content and structure of our school science curricula are generally incongruent with the ideals of the scientific enterprise. By neglecting the kinds of instructional activities that make purposeful connections between the study and practice of science, we fail to help students understand the true spirit of science, as described in these pages.

In limiting opportunities for true science learning, our nation is producing a generation of students who lack the intellectual skills necessary to assess the validity of evidence or the logic of arguments, and who are misinformed about the nature of scientific endeavors. The NAEP data support a growing body of literature urging fundamental reforms in science education—reforms in which students learn to use the tools of science to better understand the world that surrounds them.

PART I

Tilting the Balance?

Trends in Science Proficiency

Overview of Trend Results

. . . it appears that students at ages 9 and 13 have started up the road to recovery.

THE RESULTS from NAEP's 1986 science assessment indicate recent improvements at all three age levels assessed. Although the patterns are subtle, it appears that students at ages 9 and 13 have started up the road to recovery. At age 17, students showed their first statistically significant improvements after more than a decade of steady declines. These signs of progress are encouraging and reinforce trends prevalent in several recent national surveys, but the question remains whether the recent upturns in performance represent the beginning of sustained positive trends leading back to and even beyond prior achievement levels, or only an abatement of previous declines.

Another cloud hangs over the positive findings in the trend lines. In addition to their subtle and possibly tenuous nature, the recent improvements occurred only in lower-level skills and basic science knowledge. While average science proficiency is on the rise, students in the upper range of science proficiency did not show any improvement—nor are there increasing percentages of these students. Performance on moderately complex and

19

specialized scientific tasks has not changed in almost a decade, and only a small number of students—merely 7 percent of the 17-year-olds—demonstrated such higher-level skills.

The cloud's silver lining may be found in the gains shown by traditionally "at-risk" student populations. Black and Hispanic students and students living in the Southeast continued to make progress in narrowing their substantial gap in performance compared to other groups of students. However, the results for females were not so encouraging. Although the historical gender gap may be shrinking at age 17, it appears to be increasing at the younger ages.

Although the historical gender gap may be shrinking at age 17, it appears to be increasing at the younger ages.

Summary of Assessment Procedures

This report chronicles trends in proficiency across five science assessments conducted in the academic years 1969-70, 1972-73, 1976-77, 1981-82, and 1985-86. Each of the five science assessments involved nationally representative samples of 9- and 13-year-olds, and in-school 17-year-olds, and together the assessments generated data from a total of 241,256 students for the examination of trends. For convenience, each of the four most recent assessments will be referred to by the last half of the school year in which it occurred—1973, 1977, 1982, and 1986. However, the 1969-70 assessment will be referred to as such, since 9- and 13-year-olds were assessed in 1970, and 17-year-olds were assessed in 1969. It should also be noted that the 1982 assessment was carried out through a special grant from the National Science Foundation to the University of Minnesota.[1]

The data were analyzed using Item Response Theory (IRT) scaling technology and were summarized on a common scale (0 to 500) to enable direct comparisons across assessment years for age groups and demographic subpopulations. To provide a basis for interpreting the results, the report describes what students attaining different proficiency levels on the scale are able to do. Based on the assessment results, five levels of proficiency were defined:

Level 150—Knows Everyday Science Facts

Level 200—Understands Simple Scientific Principles

Level 250—Applies Basic Scientific Information

Level 300—Analyzes Scientific Procedures and Data

Level 350—Integrates Specialized Scientific Information

---

[1]Stacey J. Hueftle, Steven J. Rakow, and Wayne W. Welch, *Images of Science: A Summary of Results from the 1981-82 National Assessment of Science* (Minneapolis, MN: Science Assessment and Research Project, University of Minnesota, 1983).

NAEP's science scale was computed as the weighted composite of proficiency on five content-area subscales—**Nature of Science, Life Sciences, Chemistry, Physics, and Earth and Space Sciences**. Thus, for the 1986 assessment, results are also available indicating students' relative strengths and weaknesses across these content areas.

The terms "proficiency" and "achievement" as they are used in this report refer specifically to performance on the items comprising the NAEP science scale. To measure students' science proficiency, the assessment included both open-ended and multiple-choice questions covering a wide range of content and process areas, as well as a variety of contexts. Student background information gathered during each assessment administration permits consideration of performance trends in relation to school, home, and attitudinal factors.

Student background information gathered during each assessment administration permits consideration of performance trends in relation to school, home, and attitudinal factors.

The most recent NAEP science assessments did not include measures of students' ability to "do" science—that is, their ability to use laboratory equipment and apply higher-order thinking skills in experimental situations. Until additional resources are available to build on the work of NAEP's 1986 pilot study of hands-on activities, NAEP science assessments must continue to approximate students' higher-order thinking and laboratory skills from their performance on innovative pencil-and-paper tasks.[2]

Part I of this report discusses trends in science proficiency for 17-year-olds across the 17-year-period from 1969 to 1986, and for 9- and 13-year-olds across the 16-year period from 1970 to 1986. Chapter 1 presents changes in average proficiency for the nation and demographic subpopulations across the five NAEP science assessments. Chapter 2 describes the science competencies attained by students at five proficiency levels across the distribution of performance, and presents trends in the percentages of students reaching each level.

The chapters in Part II present information about the school context for science learning, including the amount and kinds of science instruction that students receive as well as their relative proficiency in five science content areas—Nature of Science, Life Sciences, Chemistry, Physics, and Earth and Space Sciences.

The chapters in Part III include information about key variables associated with learning in science, including students' science activities, their attitudes toward science, and their home environment.

---

[2]National Assessment of Educational Progress, *Learning by Doing: A Manual for Teaching and Assessing Higher-Order Thinking in Science and Mathematics* (Princeton, NJ : Educational Testing Service, 1987).

A Note on Interpretations

Interpreting the assessment results—attempting to put them into a "real world" context, advancing plausible explanations of results, and suggesting possible courses of action—will always be an art, not a science. No one can control all the possible variables affecting a survey. Also, any particular change in proficiency may be explainable in many ways or perhaps not at all. The interpretative remarks in this report reflect the professional judgments of NAEP staff and consultants; however, they do not necessarily reflect the views of every individual who participated in the writing of the report. Rather, these conjectures represent one way of stimulating the debate necessary to achieve a full understanding of the findings and to implement appropriate action. As such, they must stand the tests of reason and the reader's knowledge and experience.

CHAPTER 1
The Road to Recovery

Trends in Average Science Proficiency for the Nation and Demographic Subgroups

National Trends: 1970-1986

T HIS CHAPTER presents trends in average science proficiency across five national assessments for 9- and, 13-year-olds and in-school 17-year-olds on a single scale ranging from 0 to 500.[1] To provide meaning for student performance on the science proficiency scale, NAEP has also characterized what students know and can do at five different levels on the scale: Level 150—Knows Everyday Science Facts, Level 200—Understands Simple Scientific Principles, Level 250—Applies Basic Scientific Information, Level 300—Analyzes Scientific Procedures and Data, and Level 350—Integrates Specialized Scientific Information. Trends in performance at each of these levels are provided in Chapter 2.

FIGURE 1.1 provides an overall index of national trends in science proficiency at ages 9, 13, and 17; for 17-year-olds, the assessments span the

---

[1]Computed as a weighted composite of student performance on five content area subscales (i.e., Life Sciences, Chemistry, Physics, Earth and Space Sciences, and the Nature of Science), the NAEP science scale takes the form of a hypothetical 500-item test comprised of questions reflecting the proportional weighting of the subscales. The scaling procedure takes into account both the characteristics of the students, as reflected by their performance on the assessment items, and the characteristics of the items themselves.

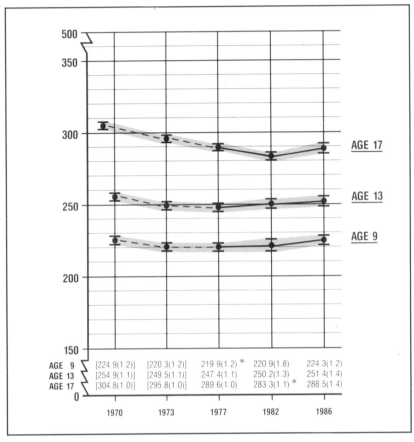

	1970	1973	1977	1982	1986
AGE 9	[224.9(1.2)]	[220.3(1.2)]	219.9(1.2) *	220.9(1.8)	224.3(1.2)
AGE 13	[254.9(1.1)]	[249.5(1.1)]	247.4(1.1)	250.2(1.3)	251.4(1.4)
AGE 17	[304.8(1.0)]	[295.8(1.0)]	289.6(1.0)	283.3(1.1) *	288.5(1.4)

[— — —] Extrapolations based on previous NAEP analyses.

 * Statistically significant difference from 1986 at the .05 level.
Jackknifed standard errors are presented in parentheses.

† Note: While 9- and 13-year-olds were assessed in the spring of 1970.
17-year-olds were assessed in the spring of 1969.

 95% CONFIDENCE INTERVAL

THE NATION'S
REPORT
CARD

17-year period from 1969 to 1986, and for 9- and 13-year-olds, the 16-year period from 1970 to 1986. Results for the 1977, 1982, and 1986 assessments are based on a newly developed trend analysis of the data collected in those years, while the results for the earlier assessments in 1969 (17-year-olds only), 1970 (9- and 13-year-olds), and 1973 (all age groups) are extrapolated from previous analyses of NAEP data.[2] (Please refer to the Procedural Appendix for details on the scaling and extrapolation methodology and a comparison of results using previous analytic methods.)

Nine-year-olds. Primarily as a result of improved performance since 1982, 9-year-olds showed small but significant gains in science proficiency during the nine-year period from 1977 to 1986. In the 16-year span covered by NAEP's five science assessments, their performance declined slightly in the early 1970s, remained quite stable through the late 1970s, then improved between 1982 and 1986. With these recent gains, the average proficiency of 9-year-olds in 1986 returned to that of the first science assessment in 1970.

Thirteen-year-olds. Trends at age 13 were similar to those at age 9, although the performance of 13-year-olds appears to have declined more and recovered less across the assessment years. After negative trends in the early 1970s that continued until 1977, 13-year-olds showed some improvement in proficiency from 1977 to 1982, but these gains did not continue to 1986. As a result, average performance at this age level in 1986 still remained slightly below that of 1970.

Seventeen-year-olds. At age 17, science performance dropped steadily from 1969 to 1982, but improved significantly from 1982 to 1986. Although the recent gains are encouraging, performance in 1986 remains well below that of the first national science assessment of 17-year-olds in 1969.

Considering the dismal impressions that have been conveyed about science achievement in our country, particularly compared with other countries, the NAEP data indicate some hope for future improvements in science education.[3] The pervasive declines posted in the early 1970s seem to have abated and students at all three ages have shown recent improvements, the most substantial of these being the upturn shown by 17-year-olds after more than a decade of steady declines. At ages 9 and 13, the patterns of decline have been less pronounced and recovery more complete.

These recent NAEP science trends reinforce an increasing body of information suggesting educational recovery in our country. Recent results from a number of large-scale surveys, including the NAEP trends in mathematics and writing, and the modest upturn in mathematics SAT scores, indicate that national declines in student test scores may be subsiding and we may be

---

[2]National Assessment of Educational Progress, *Three National Assessments of Science: Changes in Achievement, 1969-77* (Denver, CO: Education Commission of the States, 1978).

Stacey J. Hueftle, Steven J. Rakow, and Wayne W. Welch, *Images of Science: A Summary of Results from the 1981-82 National Assessment of Science* (Minneapolis, MN: Science Assessment and Research Project, University of Minnesota, 1983).

[3]International Association for the Evaluation of Educational Achievement, *Science Achievement in 17 Countries: A Preliminary Report* (New York, NY: Teachers College, Columbia University, 1988).

experiencing the beginning of a positive trend back to or even beyond previous achievement levels.[4]

The patterns of improvement in science achievement across assessments are strikingly similar to those found in the NAEP mathematics assessments.[5] In both curriculum areas, 9-year-olds showed slight improvements in the late 1970s followed by larger gains in performance between 1982 and 1986; 13-year-olds tended to show most of their improvement from the late 1970s to 1982; and 17-year-olds showed significant improvement between 1982 and 1986 after a long period of declines.

The trends in achievement for birth-year cohorts of students were also similar in science and mathematics; that is, samples of students born in the same year and assessed at ages 9, 13, and 17 as they moved through school had similar patterns of improvement and decline in both subject areas. For example, 13-year-olds born in 1968 performed better in 1982 than 13-year-olds born in 1963 had performed five years earlier; those students born in 1968 also performed better at age 17 than those born earlier.

Thus, it might be argued that the recent declines and improvements in performance at age 17 trace back to junior high school; that is, the gains seen among 17-year-olds between 1982 and 1986 may reflect improvements made by 13-year-old students between 1977 and 1982. This suggests that at least some of the factors underlying the recent upturn in performance at age 17 predated current educational reforms being implemented in high schools. A similar pattern of declines and improvements across birth-year cohorts is not reflected as clearly in the science results for 9-year-olds; however, this is not particularly surprising, considering the lack of curricular attention to this subject in elementary schools.[6]

---

[4]Arthur N. Applebee, Judith A. Langer, and Ina V.S. Mullis, *Writing Trends Across the Decade, 1974-84* (Princeton, NJ: National Assessment of Educational Progress, Educational Testing Service, 1986).

College Board, *National Report, College Bound Seniors, 1987 Profile of SAT and Achievement Test Takers* (New York, NY: College Board, 1987).

Congressional Budget Office, *Educational Achievement: Explanations and Implications of Recent Trends* (Washington, DC: Congressional Budget Office, 1987).

National Assessment of Educational Progress, *The Reading Report Card: Progress Toward Excellence in Our Schools; Trends in Reading over Four National Assessments, 1971-1984* (Princeton, NJ: Educational Testing Service, 1985).

Donald Rock et al., *Excellence in High School Education Cross-Sectional Study, 1972-1980, Final Report* (Princeton, NJ: Educational Testing Service, 1984).

William Turnbull, *Student Change, Program Change: Why SAT Scores Kept Falling* (New York, NY: College Board, Report N0. 85-2, 1985).

[5]John A. Dossey, Ina V.S. Mullis, Mary M. Lindquist, and Donald L. Chambers, *The Mathematics Report Card: Are We Measuring Up? Trends and Achievement Based on the 1986 National Assessment* (Princeton, NJ: Educational Testing Service, 1988).

[6]Iris Weiss, *Report of the 1985-86 National Survey of Science and Mathematics Education* (Research Triangle Park, NC: Research Triangle Institute, 1987). Also see Chapter 3 of this report for a discussion of NAEP findings on amount of science instruction.

Trends in Science Proficiency for Demographic Subgroups

Although the national results from the 1986 science assessment indicate improvements in average performance at all three ages, some subgroups of our population showed more improvement than others. Generally, the largest gains have been made by groups of students often considered to be at-risk, including Black and Hispanic students and students living in the Southeast. Although these recent improvements have appreciably narrowed differences in performance across subpopulations, the gaps still remain substantial.

Trends in Science Proficiency by Race/Ethnicity

FIGURE 1.2 displays trends in average science proficiency for White, Hispanic, and Black students. At all three ages, both White and Black students tended to show declines from 1969-70 to 1973. This negative trend continued until 1977, although somewhat abated, for all except Black 13-year-olds, whose performance improved from 1973 to 1977 but remained below the 1970 level. (Data are not available for Hispanic students from 1970 to 1973.)

Generally, the largest gains have been made by groups of students often considered to be at-risk, including Black and Hispanic students and students living in the Southeast.

Ages 9, 13, and 17: Trends in Average
Science Proficiency by Race/Ethnicity, 1969-70 to 1986 †

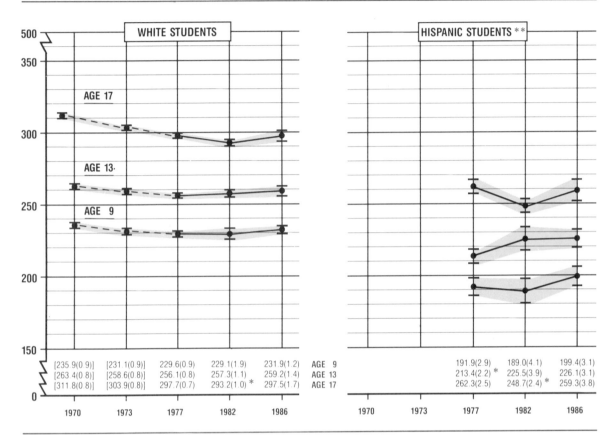

	1970	1973	1977	1982	1986	
	[235.9(0.9)]	[231.1(0.9)]	229.6(0.9)	229.1(1.9)	231.9(1.2)	AGE 9
	[263.4(0.8)]	[258.6(0.8)]	256.1(0.8)	257.3(1.1)	259.2(1.4)	AGE 13
	[311.8(0.8)]	[303.9(0.8)]	297.7(0.7)	293.2(1.0) *	297.5(1.7)	AGE 17

Hispanic students:

	1977	1982	1986	
	191.9(2.9)	189.0(4.1)	199.4(3.1)	AGE 9
	213.4(2.2) *	225.5(3.9)	226.1(3.1)	AGE 13
	262.3(2.5)	248.7(2.4) *	259.3(3.8)	AGE 17

[− − −] Extrapolations based on previous NAEP analyses.

* Statistically significant difference from 1986 at the .05 level. Jackknifed standard errors are presented in parentheses.

** 1970 and 1973 data are unavailable for Hispanic students.

† Note: While 9- and 13-year-olds were assessed in the spring of 1970, 17-year-olds were assessed in the spring of 1969.

From 1977 to 1986, White students at ages 9 and 13 tended to show slight improvement, while both Black and Hispanic students at these age levels showed larger gains. Among 17-year-olds, the negative trend in achievement continued until 1982 for White and Black students, and a parallel decline was found from 1977 to 1982 for Hispanic students. Although all three subgroups at age 17 improved significantly from 1982 to 1986, only Black students showed significant gains across the nine-year span from 1977 to 1986. As a result of recent improvements, Black students surpassed their 1977 performance in 1986, while Hispanic and White students did not.

Although all three subgroups at age 17 improved significantly from 1982 to 1986, only Black students showed significant gains across the nine-year span from 1977 to 1986.

FIGURE 1.2

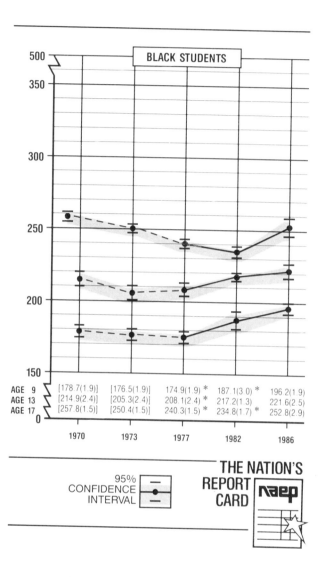

	1970	1973	1977	1982	1986
AGE 9	[178.7(1.9)]	[176.5(1.9)]	174.9(1.9) *	187.1(3.0) *	196.2(1.9)
AGE 13	[214.9(2.4)]	[205.3(2.4)]	208.1(2.4) *	217.2(1.3)	221.6(2.5)
AGE 17	[257.8(1.5)]	[250.4(1.5)]	240.3(1.5) *	234.8(1.7) *	252.8(2.9)

95% CONFIDENCE INTERVAL

THE NATION'S REPORT CARD

Minority students at ages 13 and 17 still appear to perform, on average, at least four years behind their majority counterparts.

Although substantially larger gains by Black and Hispanic students served to narrow their performance gaps relative to White students, the remaining disparities are a serious concern. Minority students at ages 13 and 17 still appear to perform, on average, at least four years behind their majority counterparts. In 1986, Black and Hispanic 13-year-old students showed average science proficiency below that of White 9-year-old students, and the average proficiency of Black and Hispanic 17-year-old students was at or below that of White 13-year-old students.

FIGURE 1.3

Ages 9, 13, and 17: Trends in Average
Science Proficiency by Gender, 1969-70 to 1986 †

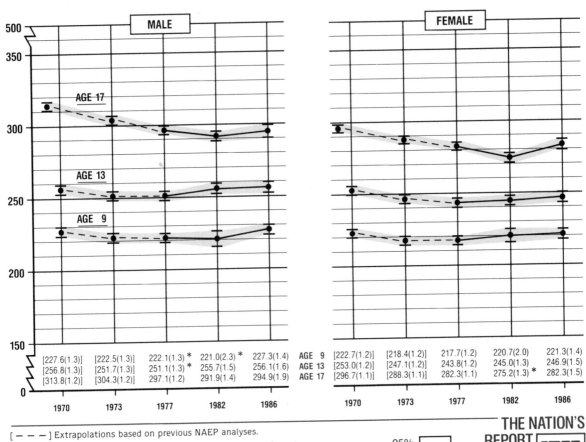

	1970	1973	1977	1982	1986	
	[227.6(1.3)]	[222.5(1.3)]	222.1(1.3) *	221.0(2.3) *	227.3(1.4)	AGE 9
	[256.8(1.3)]	[251.7(1.3)]	251.1(1.3) *	255.7(1.5)	256.1(1.6)	AGE 13
	[313.8(1.2)]	[304.3(1.2)]	297.1(1.2)	291.9(1.4)	294.9(1.9)	AGE 17

	1970	1973	1977	1982	1986
[222.7(1.2)]	[218.4(1.2)]	217.7(1.2)	220.7(2.0)	221.3(1.4)
[253.0(1.2)]	[247.1(1.2)]	243.8(1.2)	245.0(1.3)	246.9(1.5)
[296.7(1.1)]	[288.3(1.1)]	282.3(1.1)	275.2(1.3) *	282.3(1.5)

[— — —] Extrapolations based on previous NAEP analyses.

* Statistically significant difference from 1986 at the .05 level.
  Jackknifed standard errors are presented in parentheses.

† Note: While 9- and 13-year-olds were assessed in the spring of 1970.
  17-year-olds were assessed in the spring of 1969.

95%
CONFIDENCE
INTERVAL

THE NATION'S
REPORT
CARD **naep**

Trends in Science Proficiency by Gender

FIGURE 1.3 provides trends in science proficiency for males and females in each age group assessed. At all three ages, and particularly at age 17, the science proficiency of females in 1986 was below that of males, continuing a pattern from earlier assessments. However, trends in average proficiency have differed for males and females, producing varied effects on the performance gaps at each age level.

The average science proficiency of 9-year-old males declined from 1970 to 1973, remained relatively stable until 1982, then improved significantly in 1986, thus returning to the level of the first science assessment. In comparison, the science performance of 9-year-old females declined through 1977, improved in 1982, and stabilized in 1986; as a result, their average proficiency in 1986 remained slightly below that of 1970. Viewed as a whole, the results indicate that the performance gap between males and females at age 9 has increased somewhat across time.

The average proficiency of 13-year-old males declined from 1970 to 1977, but as a result of significant gains since 1977, their performance returned in 1986 to the level of the 1970 assessment. Females at this age showed a similar pattern, but their proficiency declined more than that of males between 1970 and 1977, and improved less between 1977 and 1986; consequently, the performance gap between 13-year-old males and females appears to have more than doubled across the five assessments.

At age 17, trends in performance were comparable for males and females, with both groups showing steady declines in performance from 1969 to 1982, and improvements from 1982 to 1986. Because the improvement shown by 17-year-old females was statistically significant and that shown by males was not, the disparity between males and females may have been narrowed slightly from 1969 to 1986.

... the performance gap between 13-year-old males and females appears to have more than doubled across the five assessments.

31

Ages 9, 13, and 17: Trends in Average
Science Proficiency by Region, 1969-70 to 1986†

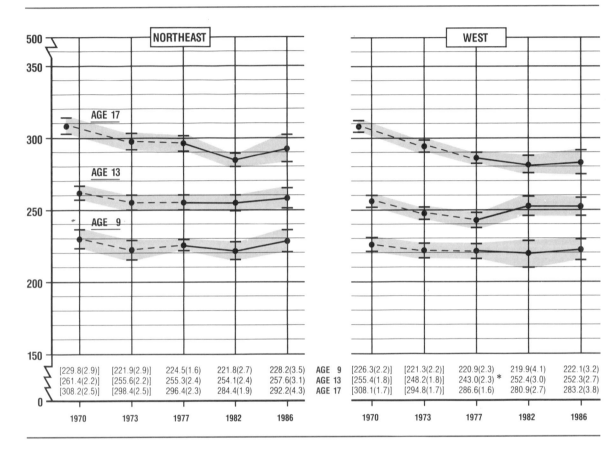

	NORTHEAST						WEST			
[229.8(2.9)]	[221.9(2.9)]	224.5(1.6)	221.8(2.7)	228.2(3.5)	**AGE 9**	[226.3(2.2)]	[221.3(2.2)]	220.9(2.3)	219.9(4.1)	222.1(3.2)
[261.4(2.2)]	[255.6(2.2)]	255.3(2.4)	254.1(2.4)	257.6(3.1)	**AGE 13**	[255.4(1.8)]	[248.2(1.8)]	243.0(2.3) *	252.4(3.0)	252.3(2.7)
[308.2(2.5)]	[298.4(2.5)]	296.4(2.3)	284.4(1.9)	292.2(4.3)	**AGE 17**	[308.1(1.7)]	[294.8(1.7)]	286.6(1.6)	280.9(2.7)	283.2(3.8)
1970	1973	1977	1982	1986		1970	1973	1977	1982	1986

[— — —] Extrapolations based on previous NAEP analyses.

* Statistically significant difference from 1986 at the .05 level. Jackknifed standard errors are presented in parentheses.

†Note: While 9- and 13-year-olds were assessed in the spring of 1970, 17-year-olds were assessed in the spring of 1969.

Trends in Science Proficiency by Region

Regional trends for NAEP's five science assessments are presented in FIGURE 1.4. (See Procedural Appendix for definition of regions.) Trends in performance have been erratic for students living in the Northeast. After initial declines, the performance of 9- and 13-year-olds in this region fluctuated through the mid-1970s before showing slight gains between 1982 and 1986. The performance of 17-year-old students from the Northeast declined

FIGURE 1.4

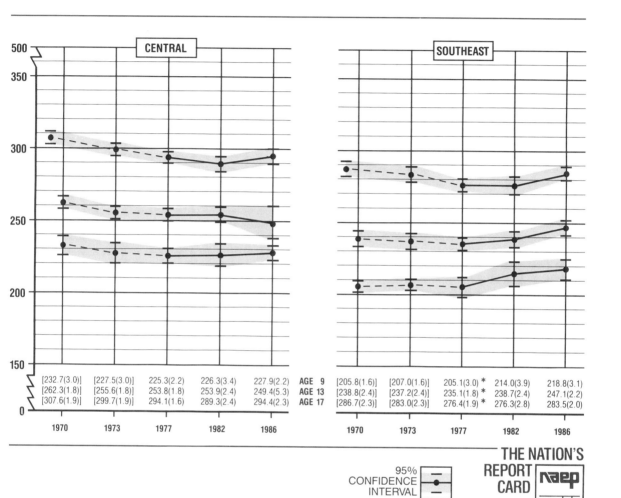

[232.7(3.0)]	[227.5(3.0)]	225.3(2.2)	226.3(3.4)	227.9(2.2)	**AGE 9**	
[262.3(1.8)]	[255.6(1.8)]	253.8(1.8)	253.9(2.4)	249.4(5.3)	**AGE 13**	
[307.6(1.9)]	[299.7(1.9)]	294.1(1.6)	289.3(2.4)	294.4(2.3)	**AGE 17**	

CENTRAL — 1970, 1973, 1977, 1982, 1986

SOUTHEAST:

[205.8(1.6)]	[207.0(1.6)]	205.1(3.0) *	214.0(3.9)	218.8(3.1)
[238.8(2.4)]	[237.2(2.4)]	235.1(1.8) *	238.7(2.4)	247.1(2.2)
[286.7(2.3)]	[283.0(2.3)]	276.4(1.9) *	276.3(2.8)	283.5(2.0)

SOUTHEAST — 1970, 1973, 1977, 1982, 1986

95% CONFIDENCE INTERVAL

THE NATION'S REPORT CARD naep

steadily between 1969 and 1982, before partially recovering in 1986. Thus, despite the fact that all three age groups in the Northeast exhibited some recent improvement, long-term trends indicate that the performance of 9- and 13-year-olds in this region was no better in 1986 than it was in 1969-70 — and the performance of 17-year-olds was considerably worse.

As with trends in the Northeast, recent changes in science performance in the Central region have been uneven. At age 9, students' performance tended to decline through 1977, then remained relatively constant until 1986. The performance of 13-year-old students from this region declined in the early 1970s, appeared to level off until 1982, and then declined further in 1986. Trends for 17-year-olds in the Central region mirrored those for the nation, as performance declined steadily through 1982 and then recovered somewhat in 1986. At all three ages, average proficiency in 1986 failed to reach the levels seen in 1969-70.

Trends in science proficiency for 9-year-olds living in the West indicate gradual declines from 1970 to 1982, followed by relatively stable performance from 1982 to 1986. At age 13, performance declined steadily from 1970 to 1977 and then improved significantly between 1977 and 1986. The performance of 17-year-olds in the West declined sharply from 1969 to 1982 before showing signs of slight recovery in 1986. As a result of these trends, average proficiency at all three ages remained below that of 1969-70.

Although average performance in the Southeast still remains below that of other regions at all three age groups, students have shown considerable gains in recent assessments. At age 9, students' proficiency remained relatively stable between 1970 and 1977, and then rose steadily from 1977 to 1986. Thirteen-year-olds showed slight declines in performance through 1977 before posting significant gains between 1977 and 1986. The average proficiency of 17-year-olds in the Southeast declined from 1969 to 1977, but improved significantly between 1977 and 1986. Thus, at all three ages, students living in the Southeast showed significant progress across the three most recent assessments. In addition, 9- and 13-year-olds assessed in 1986 surpassed their average proficiency of 1970, and 17-year-olds nearly returned to theirs of 1969.

With the exception of these significant gains between 1977 and 1986 for 9-, 13-, and 17-year-old students in the Southeast, trends across the regions closely resembled those for the nation as a whole, following a pattern of initial declines from 1969-70 to 1973, relatively small changes through the early 1980s, and signs of recent improvements.

Summary

The results of NAEP's five science assessments indicate a national pattern of decline and recovery at all three ages assessed. However, the older the students, the greater the declines and, thus, the lesser the progress toward recovery. After declines from 1970 to 1977, 9-year-old students showed significant gains between 1977 and 1986, primarily because of a rise in performance between 1982 and 1986. These gains served to bring their average performance in 1986 back to the level of the 1970 assessment.

At age 13, student performance declined from 1970 to 1977, and then improved between 1977 and 1982; however, as trends at this age remained

Although average performance in the Southeast still remains below that of other regions ... students in the Southeast have shown considerable gains in recent assessments.

The results of NAEP's five science assessments indicate a national pattern of decline and recovery at all three ages assessed.

fairly stable from 1982 to 1986, 13-year-olds assessed in 1986 did not recover the level of proficiency they exhibited in 1970. After more than a decade of declines, 17-year-olds showed significant gains between 1982 and 1986, indicating at least an abatement in their previous downward trend, if not the beginning of an upward trend. Despite these recent gains, the average performance of 17-year-olds in 1986 remained substantially lower than that shown in 1969.

While White students' performance improved slightly across recent assessments, the bulk of the progress shown by 9- and 13-year-olds in the national results can be attributed to Black and Hispanic students. At age 17, students in all three racial/ethnic groups mirrored the national trends, declining between 1969 and 1982 and then improving significantly between 1982 and 1986. Despite these substantial gains, the average science proficiency of Black and Hispanic 17-year-olds in 1986 remained well below that of their White peers; in addition, none of these racial/ethnic subpopulations in the 1986 assessment recovered the level of performance displayed in 1969. For White students, the recovery in 1986 reestablished the level of performance shown in 1977. Hispanic 17-year-olds nearly recovered their 1977 level of performance in 1986. In contrast, Black 17-year-olds assessed in 1986 showed a large net gain over their 1977 performance, improving significantly across the nine-year period.

The performance gap between males and females has remained substantial across time, and while it may be decreasing slightly at age 17, the gap appears to be increasing for the younger students, particularly at age 13. Males at the younger ages improved their science performance significantly between 1977 and 1986, whereas females did not. In contrast, the gains shown between 1982 and 1986 at age 17 were statistically significant for females, but not for males.

The performance of students living in the Southeast improved significantly from 1977 to 1986 for all three age groups; as a result, 9- and 13-year-olds from this region surpassed their 1970 performance in 1986, while 17-year-olds nearly recovered their 1969 performance. Changes in the other three regions generally reflected national patterns.

Overall, recent trends are encouraging, and it is hoped that the ambitious efforts of the current educational reform movement foreshadow continued gains in science proficiency. Viewing the 1986 findings in their historical context, however, it is clear that much greater effort is needed to return performance at least to the level observed in the 1969 and 1970 assessments—which even then may have been lower than expected.

CHAPTER 2
What Students Know About Science

Levels of Science Proficiency for the Nation and Demographic Subgroups

Defining Levels of Proficiency

DISCUSSIONS ABOUT improving science education tend to center on two important goals: ensuring that all students have the opportunity to gain the scientific literacy needed to function in and contribute to society as informed decision-makers *and* providing a sufficient number of young Americans with the scientific and technological expertise necessary for our nation to retain or improve its place in the global economy.

To provide information on our country's progress toward these goals, NAEP used the range of student performance in the assessment to describe five levels of science proficiency on the scale presented in Chapter 1:

Level 150—Knows Everyday Science Facts

Level 200—Understands Simple Scientific Principles

Level 250—Applies Basic Scientific Information

Level 300—Analyzes Scientific Procedures and Data

Level 350—Integrates Specialized Scientific Information

Although proficiency levels above and below this range could theoretically have been defined, so few students in the assessment performed at the extreme ends of the scale that it was not possible in practice to define proficiency levels below 150 or above 350.

To characterize the proficiency levels, science specialists analyzed the types of items that discriminated between adjacent performance levels and described the skills held by students performing at each of the five anchor points. The descriptions of the five levels of performance were further discussed and reviewed by NAEP's panel of science consultants.

Performance levels on the scale can be characterized as the interaction between knowing about science and gaining the ability to "do" science, as well as using scientific information to infer relationships and draw conclusions. Students had little difficulty with questions about basic science facts, particularly if they entailed information likely to be encountered in everyday experiences or were related to the Life Sciences. Yet as they encountered questions that asked them to apply their knowledge and to deal with more specialized information, performance decreased.

> Students had little difficulty with questions about basic science facts, particularly if they entailed information likely to be encountered in everyday experiences or were related to the Life Sciences.

FIGURE 2.1 provides a brief characterization of performance at each anchor point on the scale. Assessment items representative of each level of performance are subsequently provided, together with the discussion of results. It should be emphasized that the sample items presented here are illustrative of the skills, knowledge, and understandings included in the science assessment, and are not intended to be inclusive of what students should know about or be capable of doing in science.

Level 150—Knows Everyday Science Facts

Students at this level know some general scientific facts of the type that could be learned from everyday experiences. They can read simple graphs, match the distinguishing characteristics of animals, and predict the operation of familiar apparatus that work according to mechanical principles.

Level 200—Understands Simple Scientific Principles

Students at this level are developing some understanding of simple scientific principles, particularly in the Life Sciences. For example, they exhibit some rudimentary knowledge of the structure and function of plants and animals.

Level 250—Applies Basic Scientific Information

Students at this level can interpret data from simple tables and make inferences about the outcomes of experimental procedures. They exhibit knowledge and understanding of the Life Sciences, including a familiarity with some aspects of animal behavior and of ecological relationships. These students also demonstrate some knowledge of basic information from the Physical Sciences.

Level 300—Analyzes Scientific Procedures and Data

Students at this level can evaluate the appropriateness of the design of an experiment. They have more detailed scientific knowledge, and the skill to apply their knowledge in interpreting information from text and graphs. These students also exhibit a growing understanding of principles from the Physical Sciences.

Level 350—Integrates Specialized Scientific Information

Students at this level can infer relationships and draw conclusions using detailed scientific knowledge from the Physical Sciences, particularly Chemistry. They also can apply basic principles of genetics and interpret the societal implications of research in this field.

THE NATION'S
REPORT
CARD
naep

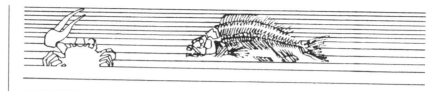

In examining trends in science proficiency, it is informative to determine what groups of students are demonstrating improved performance and in which subject areas. Are the best students becoming even more proficient? Are more students acquiring fundamental skills? Or are increases evenly spread across the range of student performance? To address these questions, the percentages of students at ages 9, 13, and 17 that attained each level of proficiency in the 1977, 1982, and 1986 assessments are displayed in TABLE 2.1.

Ages 9, 13, and 17: Trends in the Percentage of Students at or Above the Five Proficiency Levels, 1977-1986

TABLE 2.1

		Assessment Year		
Proficiency Levels	Age	1977	1982	1986
Level 150	9	93.6 (0.5)*	95.0 (0.5)	96.3 (0.3)
Knows Everyday	13	98.6 (0.1)	99.6 (0.1)	99.8 (0.1)
Science Facts	17	99.8 (0.0)	99.7 (0.1)	99.9 (0.1)
Level 200	9	67.9 (1.1)*	70.4 (1.6)	71.4 (1.0)
Understands Simple	13	85.9 (0.7)*	89.6 (0.7)	91.8 (0.9)
Scientific Principles	17	97.2 (0.2)	95.8 (0.4)	96.7 (0.4)
Level 250	9	26.2 (0.7)	24.8 (1.7)	27.6 (1.0)
Applies Basic	13	49.2 (1.1)*	51.5 (1.4)	53.4 (1.4)
Scientific Information	17	81.8 (0.7)	76.8 (1.0)*	80.8 (1.2)
Level 300	9	3.5 (0.2)	2.2 (0.6)	3.4 (0.4)
Analyzes Scientific	13	10.9 (0.4)	9.4 (0.6)	9.4 (0.7)
Procedures and Data	17	41.7 (0.8)	37.5 (0.8)*	41.4 (1.4)
Level 350	9	0.0 (0.0)	0.1 (0.1)	0.1 (0.1)
Integrates Specialized	13	0.7 (0.1)	0.4 (0.1)	0.2 (0.1)
Scientific Information	17	8.5 (0.4)	7.2 (0.4)	7.5 (0.6)

*Statistically significant difference from 1986 at the 0.5 level. No significance test is reported when the proportion of students is either >95.0 or <5.0. Jackknifed standard errors are presented in parentheses.

LEVEL 150	1986		
Knows Everyday Science Facts	Age 9	Age 13	Age 17
	96.3	99.8	99.9

In 1986, virtually all students at all three ages assessed had some science knowledge of the type that might be gained from everyday experiences, including elementary facts about the characteristics of animals and the operation of familiar mechanical devices. With the exception of slight improvement at age 9, the percentage of students at this level of performance remained essentially unchanged across the NAEP assessments conducted since 1977.

Four sample items associated with Level 150 performance are provided below.

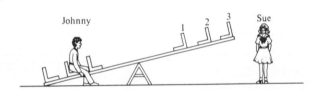

Look at the picture above. John weighs 90 pounds and Sue weighs 75 pounds. If Sue wants to make her end of the seesaw go down, should she sit at 1, or at 2, or at 3?

○ 1

○ 2

● 3

Which of the birds pictured below probably lives around ponds and eats snails and small fish?

Heron	Sparrow	Hawk	Swallow
●	○	○	○

To which of the following animals is the wolf most closely related?

- ○ Buffalo
- ○ Deer
- ● Dog
- ○ Rabbit
- ○ Sheep
- ○ I don't know.

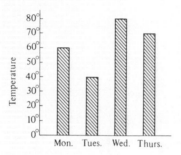

The graph above shows the high temperature on each day for four days. Which day was the hottest?

- ○ Monday
- ○ Tuesday
- ● Wednesday
- ○ Thursday

Understands Simple Scientific Principles

	1986	
Age 9	Age 13	Age 17
. 71.4	91.8	96.7

A significantly
greater proportion
of both 9- and 13-
year-olds demon-
strated knowledge
about simple sci-
entific information
in 1986 than did
in 1977.

A significantly greater proportion of both 9- and 13-year-olds demonstrated knowledge about simple scientific information in 1986 than did in 1977. In 1977, 68 percent of the 9-year-olds and 86 percent of the 13-year-olds performed at or above Level 200. Nearly all of the 17-year-olds attained this level in each of the three most recent assessments.

It is encouraging to see that a large proportion of 13- and 17-year-olds are performing at or above this level, and that progress has been made over time by students at the younger ages. However, concern must still be raised about the students at age 9—approximately 1 million third and fourth graders—who have not yet developed some understanding of scientific principles and a rudimentary knowledge of plants and animals.

Six assessment items representative of Level 200 performance are provided below.

Why may you become ill after visiting a friend who is sick with the flu?

○ The room your friend was in was too warm.

○ You ate the same kind of food your friend ate.

○ You did not dress properly.

● The virus that causes the flu entered your body.

Which of the following animals does NOT lay eggs?

○ Ostrich

○ Frog

● Mouse

○ Turtle

Some water is poured into the U-shaped glass tube shown above. Which picture below best shows how the water level will look? Fill in the oval under the picture you choose.

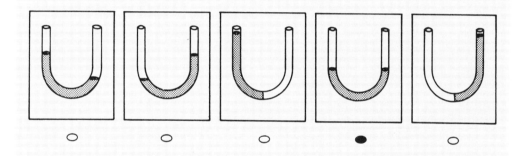

○

○   I don't know.

What is the main function of the heart?

●   To pump the blood to all parts of the body

○   To keep a person warm in winter by beating fast

○   To store extra blood until it is needed

○   To take waste food out of the blood

Which of the following plants would probably produce flowers?

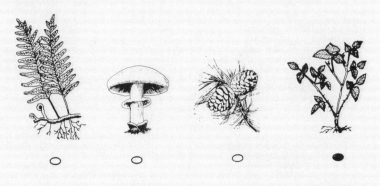

    ◯   ◯   ◯   ●

The moon produces no light, and yet it shines at night. What is the best explanation for this?

    ◯ It has many craters.

    ◯ It rotates at a very high speed.

    ◯ It is covered with a fine layer of ice.

    ● It reflects the light from the Sun.

LEVEL 250

Applies Basic Scientific Information

Age 9	Age 13	Age 17
27.6	53.4	80.8

... only relatively low percentages of the students in the two younger age groups demonstrated a basic understanding of the Life and Physical Sciences.

Without a better foundation in their middle-school years, students will likely be unprepared to take more advanced courses as they progress through high school.

Approximately the same percentages of students at ages 9 and 17 attained Level 250 in 1986 as did in 1977, but there were statistically significant increases in the percentage of 13-year-olds at this level. Despite these improvements at age 13, only relatively low percentages of the students in the two younger age groups demonstrated a basic understanding of the Life and Physical Sciences. Given the dearth of science instruction in the elementary grades (as discussed in Chapter 3), it is perhaps understandable that only slightly more than one-quarter of the 9-year-olds attained this level. However, 13-year-olds (primarily in the seventh and eighth grades) presumably have had instruction in general science, and that only about one-half of these junior-high-school students appear to have a grasp of the basic elements of science is quite disturbing. Without a better foundation in their middle-school years, students will likely be unprepared to take more advanced courses as they progress through high school. Further, the 19 percent of 17-year-olds that did not reach this level may have great difficulty as they begin their adult lives, since they lack a core understanding of scientific principles.

A series of items representative of performance at Level 250 follows.

In an ordinary light bulb with a screw-type base, which is the part that glows to produce the light?

- ● A special thin wire at the center of the light bulb
- ○ A special gas that fills the inside of the light bulb
- ○ A special type of glass that makes up the light bulb
- ○ A special paint that coats the outside of the light bulb

In which of the following pairs are both objects made from things that were once alive?

- ○ Automobile engines and bicycle handlebars
- ● Cotton thread and newspaper
- ○ China dishes and glass windows
- ○ Aluminum pots and dishwashing detergents

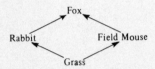

With respect to the field mouse in the food web above, what is the fox considered?

- ● A predator

- ○ A prey

- ○ A producer

- ○ A decomposer

Becky asked some friends in different grades how many books they read during the summer. Here is what Becky found.

Friend	Grade	Number of Books read
Tom	6	5
Jane	5	5
Dan	2	2
Bob	2	1
Sue	1	0

Which of the following best tells what Becky found?

- ○ The students in the lower grades read as many books as the students in the upper grades.

- ○ The students read more books in the summer.

- ○ Becky asked one student from the 6th grade and two students from the 2nd grade how many books each read.

- ● The students in the lower grades read fewer books than the students in the upper grades.

- ○ I don't know.

Ten plants were placed in sandy soil and ten others were placed in clay soil. Both groups of plants were kept at room temperature, given the same amount of water, and placed in a sunny room. This experiment tests the effect of

- ○ sunlight on plant growth.
- ○ temperature on plant growth.
- ● different soils on plant growth.
- ○ water on plant growth.

Which of the following diseases is NOT directly transmitted among people in contact with each other?

- ○ Herpes
- ○ Influenza
- ○ Tuberculosis
- ● Diabetes

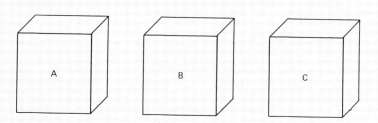

Blocks A, B, and C are the same size. Blocks B and C float on water. Block A sinks to the bottom. Which one of the following do you know is TRUE?

- ● Block A weighs more than block B.
- ○ Block B weighs more than block C.
- ○ Block C weighs more than block A.
- ○ Block B weighs more than block A.
- ○ I don't know.

Analyzes Scientific Procedures and Data

	1986	
Age 9	Age 13	Age 17
3.4	9.4	41.4

In 1986, only 3 percent of the 9-year-old students, 9 percent of the 13-year-olds, and 41 percent of the 17-year-olds demonstrated some understanding of the design of experiments or any degree of specialized knowledge across the subdisciplines of science. These results did not represent any improvement across time in performance at this level—a level that may be characterized as the sort of scientific literacy one might expect to be universally held by members of society.

The fact that a majority of 17-year-olds failed to reach Level 300 is quite alarming, and suggests that school science is not helping students learn to use their knowledge of scientific facts or principles in evaluating the appropriateness of procedures or in interpreting results. Further this figure does not include those students who have already dropped out of school by age 17. With only 1 in 10 of our junior-high school students performing at this level, it is perhaps not surprising that so few high-school students elect to enroll in advanced science courses; they may simply lack the prerequisite skills. Just as high schools are receiving students who are ill-prepared for further study of science, so they are supplying the labor force with relatively low percentages of high-school graduates with even moderate scientific understanding.

Five assessment items representative of performance at Level 300 are provided below.

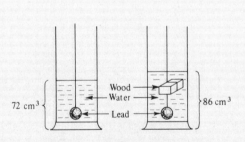

The volume of a block of wood can be found by suspending it in water, as the diagrams above show. What is the volume of the block?

- ● (86 − 72) cm³
- ○ 86 cm³
- ○ (72 − 86) cm³
- ○ (72 + 86) cm³

The new product Super Plant Food has been advertised. Claims have been made that Super Plant Food will cause plants to grow to giant sizes. Directions on the label of this new product say: "Simply add 1 teaspoon of Super Plant Food powder to each gallon of water used to water your seeds or growing plants. Plants watered with Super Plant Food solution will grow faster and become twice as large as normal plants."

Suppose you wish to test scientifically the claims of the makers of Super Plant Food. Which of the following experiments would best test whether Super Plant Food helps the growth of bean plants?

○ Place 1 bean seed in each of two identical pots of soil. Water each pot with the same amount of Super Plant Food solution each day.

○ Plant 10 bean seeds in a pot of soil. Water with the same amount of Super Plant Food solution each day.

● Plant 10 bean seeds in each of two identical pots of soil. Water one pot with a cup of Super Plant Food solution each day, and water the other pot with a cup of water each day.

○ Place 100 bean seeds on a sponge. Keep the sponge moistened with Super Plant Food solution.

Which of the following best explains why marine algae are most often restricted to the top 100 meters in the ocean?

○ They have no roots to anchor them to the ocean floor.

● They are photosynthetic and can live only where there is light.

○ The pressure is too great for them to survive below 100 meters.

○ The temperature of the top 100 meters of the ocean is ideal for them.

Which of the following is the best indication of an approaching storm?

○ A seismogram that is a straight line

● A decrease in barometric pressure

○ A clearing sky after a cold front passes

○ A sudden drop in the humidity

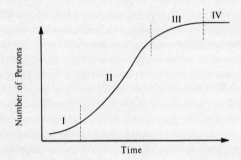

In the population growth curve above, in which interval is the population in equilibrium (the death rate equal to the birth rate)?

○   I

○   II

○   III

●   IV

LEVEL 350

Integrates Specialized Scientific Information

1986

Age 9	Age 13	Age 17
0.1	0.2	7.5

The low percentages of students performing at this level have remained constant across the three most recent NAEP assessments. Virtually no students at ages 9 and 13 reached Level 350 in 1986, and only 7 percent of the 17-year-olds did. Considering the high demand for skilled technological personnel in our nation's workforce, these results are particularly troublesome. While approximately 40 percent of the nation's high-school students have a moderate understanding of science, typified by performance at Level 300, only 7 percent have any degree of sophisticated understanding in the subject. Students attaining Level 350 are likely to represent the pool from which future scientists are drawn, and given the expected attrition in this group through subsequent academic or vocational training, the percentage of 17-year-old students reaching this level of proficiency seems to be substantially smaller than that needed for the future workforce.

Overall gains in performance exhibited in the NAEP assessments indicate that while our country may be helping more students to understand the rudiments of science—evidenced by trends in performance at the lower levels of the scale—only very small percentages of students are developing a moderate or sophisticated scientific background. The dismal findings of the second international assessment of science—indicating that in many subdisciplines of science, the performance of students from the U.S. is among the lowest of the countries assessed—reinforce the notion that our nation is not keeping up with the increased demand for men and women trained in specialized areas.[1]

Sample items indicative of performance at Level 350 follow.

Recombinant DNA research has produced a variety of organisms with big economic potential. For which of the following reasons are concerned citizens hesitant to permit the use of these organisms outside of the laboratory?

○ Production of such organisms will involve the production of hazardous by-products.

○ Most scientific research is perceived to be dangerous.

○ The organisms could die outside of a laboratory environment.

● The introduction of organisms new to the Earth could upset the ecological balance.

---

[1]International Association for the Evaluation of Educational Achievement, *Science Achievement in 17 Countries: A Preliminary Report* (New York, NY: Teachers College, Columbia University, 1988).

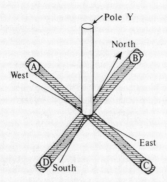

In the central United States at 8:00 a.m. on September 23 it is sunny, and the vertical pole shown in the diagram above casts a shadow. Which shaded area best approximates the position of the shadow?

● A

○ B

○ C

○ D

A female white rabbit and a male black rabbit mate and have a large number of baby rabbits. About half of the baby rabbits are black, and the other half are white. If black fur is the dominant color in rabbits, how can the appearance of white baby rabbits best be explained?

○ The female rabbit has one gene for black fur and one gene for white fur.

● The male rabbit has one gene for black fur and one gene for white fur.

○ The white baby rabbits received no genes for fur color from the father.

○ The white baby rabbits are result of accidental mutations.

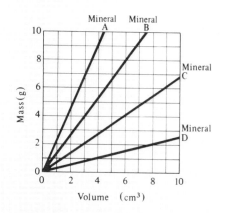

Water has a density of 1 gram per cubic centimeter. Which mineral(s) would float in water?

○ A only

○ D only

○ A and B only

● C and D only

Which of the following objects has the greatest density?

	Mass of Object	Volume of Object
○	11.0 grams	24 cubic centimeters
○	11.0 grams	12 cubic centimeters
●	5.5 grams	4 cubic centimeters
○	5.5 grams	11 cubic centimeters

$$2Na + S \rightarrow Na_2S$$

The mass of 1.0 mole of sodium, Na, is 23.0 grams. The mass of 1.0 mole of sulfur is 32.1 grams. Approximately what mass of sodium is required to react completely with 32.1 grams of sulfur in the reaction above?

    ○   11.5 grams

    ○   23.0 grams

    ○   32.0 grams

    ●   46.0 grams

Elements with chemical characteristics most similar to those of sodium are listed in what part of the periodic table?

    ○   Immediately to the right of sodium in the same row

    ○   Immediately to the left of sodium in the same row

    ●   Above and below sodium in the same column

    ○   On the far right of the periodic table

An ore sample contains 50 grams of radioisotope with a half-life of 5 seconds. After 10 seconds, how many grams of the radioisotope are in the sample?

    ●   12.5 grams

    ○   25 grams

    ○   50 grams

    ○   75 grams

Levels of Proficiency for Demographic Subgroups

Because female, Black, and Hispanic students are less likely than those who are male or White to take science courses or pursue scientific careers, issues of equity have been of major concern to science educators.[2] How much progress has our country made in this area? Are as many women and minorities as in previous years attaining high levels of science proficiency? A comparison of the percentages of students in various subpopulations reaching each of the five levels of science proficiency, and changes in these percentages across time, provide a way to address such questions.

Levels of Proficiency by Race/Ethnicity

As shown in FIGURE 2.2, at ages 13 and 17, virtually all White, Hispanic, and Black students attained Level 150 in 1986. Almost all White 9-year-olds performed at or above Level 150, as did 87 percent of the Black students and 90 percent of the Hispanic students at this age. These results represent significant progress for minority students, particularly for Black 9-year-olds; in 1977, only 73 percent of these students reached Level 150, compared to 87 percent in 1986. (Please refer to the Data Appendix for a full presentation of the trend results.)

Significant progress also was made at Level 200 between 1977 and 1986 by Black 9- and 13-year-olds, and by Hispanic 13-year-olds. In this time period, the percentage of Black students at age 9 that demonstrated an understanding of simple scientific principles rose from 28 to 45 percent; at age 13, the percentage climbed from 57 to 74. Similarly, the percentage of Hispanic 13-year-olds attaining Level 200 increased by 13 percentage points, from 63 to 76 percent. Despite these gains in 1986, discrepancies in the percentage of Black, Hispanic, and White students achieving at this level still remained great at both ages 9 and 13.

At Level 250, Black and Hispanic 17-year-olds made significant progress across recent assessments, as did White students at age 13. However, large gaps in performance across racial/ethnic groups were noticeable at this level across all three ages; in 1986, 62 percent of the White students at age 13 attained Level 250, while only 20 percent of the Black students and 28 percent of the Hispanic students did.

---

[2]Michael F. Crowley, *Women and Minorities in Science and Engineering* (Washington, DC: Division of Science Resources Studies, National Science Foundation, 1986).

Task Force on Women, Minorities, and the Handicapped in Science and Technology, *Changing America: The New Face of Science and Engineering* (Washington, DC, 1988).

Ages 9, 13, and 17: Levels of Science Proficiency
Percent at or Above Anchor Points by Race/Ethnicity, 1986

FIGURE 2.2

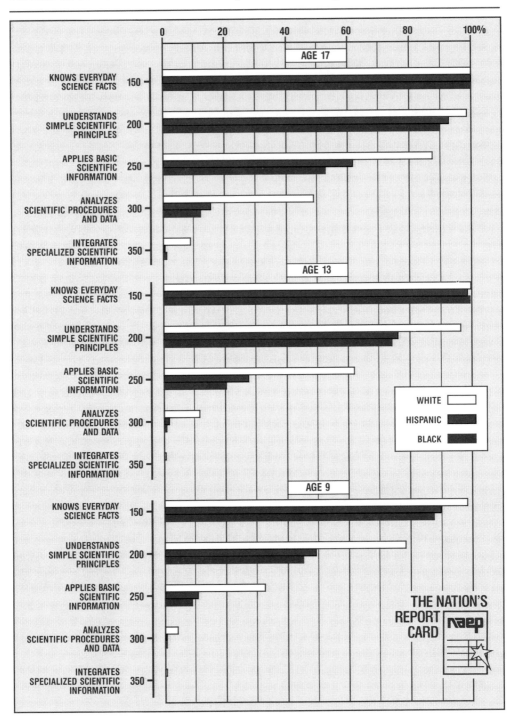

THE NATION'S REPORT CARD

At the two highest proficiency levels, the gaps in performance between majority and minority students in all three age groups remain large and have not changed significantly in recent years. In 1986, almost one-half of the White 17-year-olds reached Level 300, compared to only 15 and 12 percent of the Hispanic and Black students, respectively. At the same time, 9 percent of the White students attained Level 350, compared to only 1 percent of the Hispanic students and less than 1 percent of the Black students.

While it is encouraging that progress is being made by Black and Hispanic students . . . their performance gaps relative to White students remain appreciable and warrant serious concern.

While it is encouraging that progress is being made by Black and Hispanic students, especially at the younger ages and in the area of basic skills and knowledge, their performance gaps relative to White students remain appreciable and warrant serious concern.

Levels of Proficiency by Gender

As shown in FIGURE 2.3, which displays the 1986 results by gender, males tended to outperform females—particularly at the older ages and at the higher levels on the proficiency scale. For example, at age 17, approximately one-half of the males reached Level 300, compared to only about one-third of the females.

The trend results indicate little progress for females since 1977. The only noteworthy changes occurred at age 13, and these reflect slippage for female students. A significantly greater percentage of males at this age reached Level 250 in 1986 (58 percent, compared to 52 percent in 1977), and approximately the same proportion reached Level 300 in 1977 and 1986 (13 and 12 percent, respectively). In contrast, approximately the same percentage of 13-year-old females attained Level 250 in 1977 and 1986, and a significantly smaller percentage of females attained Level 300 (6 percent in 1986 compared to 9 percent in 1977).

It is also distressing that the gender gap increased across the three age groups. Girls in the elementary grades tended to perform as well as boys, and it is unfortunate that this equitable state of affairs has not been maintained as the two sexes moved through school. Further research is needed to discern the factors—societal, personal, educational, or other—that underlie gender differences in science proficiency and to guide appropriate interventions.

FIGURE 2.3

Ages 9, 13, and 17: Levels of Science Proficiency
Percent at or Above Anchor Points by Gender, 1986

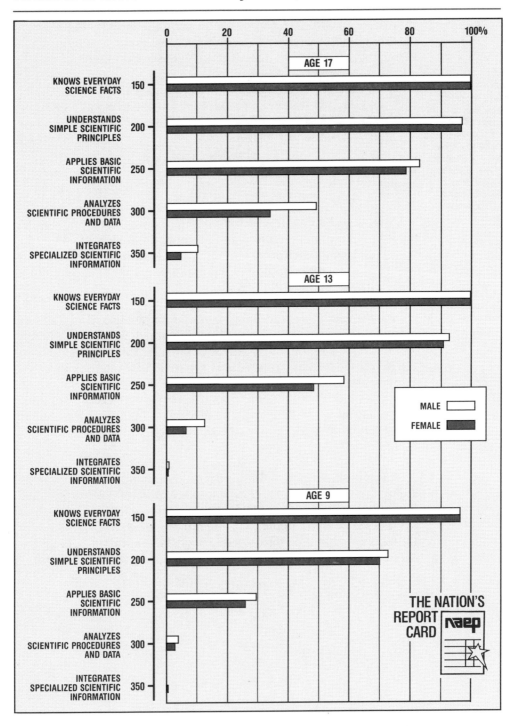

Levels of Proficiency by Region

FIGURE 2.4 presents information on the levels of proficiency attained by students from each of the four regions of the country—Northeast, Central, West, and Southeast. Although differences in regional performance are slight, students from the Northeast tended to perform the best, followed by those from the Central region, the West, and the Southeast, in descending order.

Compared with other regions, students from the Southeast are the only ones to have made progress across the proficiency levels since the 1977 science assessment. In 1986, significantly more 9-year-olds from this region reached all three of the lower proficiency levels—150, 200, and 250—and significantly more 13-year-olds reached Level 250.

Perhaps to a greater extent than most other states, the southeastern states have concentrated on rigorous educational reform in recent years, providing enhanced teacher training and career incentives, expanding assessment programs, increasing graduation requirements, strictly monitoring absenteeism, raising amounts of homework, and heightening citizen awareness[3]. Although the NAEP data do not permit identifying the factors responsible for rising science proficiency in the Southeast, the collective reform efforts in this region appear to be benefiting students' academic performance.

With the exception of the Central region—in which significantly fewer 13-year-olds reached Level 300 in 1986—performance across regions and proficiency levels was otherwise relatively stable through the assessment years.

---

[3]Denis Doyle and Terry Hartle, *Excellence in Education: The States Take Charge* (Washington, DC: American Enterprise Institute, 1985).

Ages 9, 13, and 17: Levels of Science Proficiency
Percent at or Above Anchor Points by Region, 1986

FIGURE 2.4

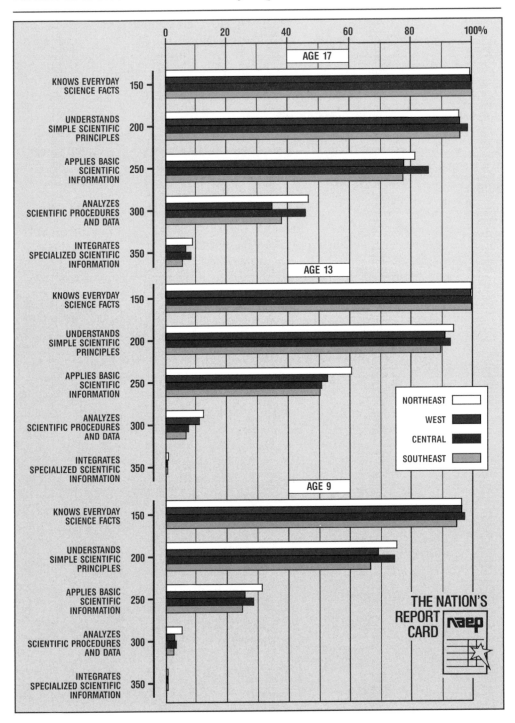

Summary

. . . the United States may be starting up the road to recovery in this subject area.

As described in Chapter 1, recent improvements in science proficiency suggest that the United States may be starting up the road to recovery in this subject area. However, the results discussed in this chapter indicate that there is much to accomplish before our country can consider itself to be at the forefront of science education. Although recent progress has been made, most has occurred at the lower end of the proficiency scale, in the areas of basic knowledge and elementary interpretation of scientific information. Not only is it necessary to increase the average science proficiency of all students in our country, but it is also essential that the percentage of students reaching the higher ranges of proficiency be increased substantially.

Students' knowledge of science and their ability to use what they know appear remarkably limited.

Students' knowledge of science and their ability to use what they know appear remarkably limited. That a very small proportion of junior-high-school students and only about 40 percent of high-school students can be considered even moderately versed in this subject area is a matter of grave concern, as is the very small percentage (7 percent) of high-school students with any degree of specialized knowledge in science. These results have serious implications for students' adult lives—including how well they will be able to participate in society as informed voters and decision makers, perform everyday tasks efficiently, express intelligent points of view, and contribute to the nation's economic future.

Minority populations and women constitute a rising proportion of the nation's labor force, and the discrepancies in performance between these groups and the nation as a whole are therefore particularly worrisome.

In today's increasingly technological society, science knowledge cannot be reserved for an elite few. All citizens need considerable scientific literacy to understand the changes in the environment, the equipment found in homes and workplaces, and the societal implications of issues such as energy, pollution, space research, and genetic engineering. Further, no country can afford to overlook large segments of its population in training the specialized personnel needed for many technologically-oriented industries. Although the progress made by Black and Hispanic students and by those living in the southeastern region of the country demonstrates movement toward equity, vast performance gaps remain across racial/ethnic groups, and essentially no progress has been made in closing the performance gap between males and females. Minority populations and women constitute a rising proportion of the nation's labor force, and the discrepancies in performance between these groups and the nation as a whole are therefore particularly worrisome.[4]

[4]Vernon Briggs, "The Growth and Composition of the U.S. Labor Force," *Science* 238 (October 1987), 176-180.

Task Force on Women, Minorities, and the Handicapped in Science and Technology, *Changing America: The New Face of Science and Engineering* (Washington, DC, 1988).

Part II

Turning the
Tide of Neglect?

The School Context for Science Learning

Introduction

CONSIDERABLE THOUGHT has been given in recent years to improving science education in this country. In *Educating Americans for the 21st Century*, a commission convened by the National Science Board recommended a number of improvements; among these were increasing the amount of instructional time committed to science, creating greater opportunities for hands-on experience, integrating new technologies into instruction, and providing more "coordination and continuity" in the science curriculum.[1]

Teachers are at the center of many of these recommendations, as they are thought to be the key to resolving many of the glaring deficiencies of the American educational system. State and federal policy makers have moved rapidly in the past decade, issuing innumerable pieces of legislation designed to strengthen teacher education and training, raise certification requirements, and increase teacher compensation.[2]

[1]National Science Board Commission on Precollege Education in Mathematics, Science, and Techonology, *Educating Americans for the 21st Century* (Washington, DC: National Science Foundation, 1983).

[2]Linda Darling-Hammond and Barnett Berry, *The Evolution of Teacher Policy* (New Brunswick, NJ: RAND Center for Policy Research in Education, 1988).

Planning for the 1986 NAEP science assessment began amidst these emerging recommendations and policies for improving science education. Accordingly, the assessment had as one of its goals to collect timely information on some of the primary concerns that have been voiced about formal science instruction. Among these are the following:

... the assessment had as one of its goals to collect timely information on some of the primary concerns that have been voiced about formal science instruction.

■ Little time is spent on science teaching in this country, particularly at the elementary-school level.

■ Enrollment is low in high-school science courses, and few students reach advanced levels of course-taking.

■ The supply of well-qualified science instructors is decreasing, according to some reports.

■ Science instruction is dominated by teacher lectures and textbook readings, rather than laboratory experiments and other hands-on activities.

The following chapters discuss these aspects of the school context for science learning. Chapter 3 summarizes data on the amount of time that teachers and students in grades 3, 7, and 11 spend on science teaching and learning. Additional information is provided on the amount and content of course work to which students in the upper grades have been exposed, and on relationships between students' general exposure to science instruction and their proficiency in the subject.

Chapter 4 describes students' performance in five science content areas specified in the assessment objectives—Life Sciences, Physics, Chemistry, Nature of Science, and Earth and Space Sciences.[3] The relationship between course-taking experience and science proficiency also is articulated, building on the discussions in Chapter 3. In Chapter 5, attention is given to the nature of science instruction, providing both student- and teacher-reported data on teaching practices and instructional activities, as well as information on teachers' qualifications to teach science.

Assessment Procedures

Background questions on course-taking, teaching practices, and instructional activities discussed in Part II of this report were administered to students at the same time and using the same procedures as those for the cognitive questions. Similarly, the background questions were administered to systematic samples of students in a way that allowed accurate estimates of responses for the nation as a whole and for subpopulations of interest. Some

---

[3]National Assessment of Educational Progress, *Science Objectives: 1985-86 Assessment* (Princeton, NJ: Educational Testing Service, 1987).

of the background questions were included for the first time in the 1986 assessment, and are therefore reported for students in grades 3, 7, and 11. The grade-level results discussed in this report are based on 11,046 students in grade 3; 12,142 students in grade 7; and 11,744 students in grade 11. Other questions were integrated from previous science assessments, permitting NAEP to report on trends for 9-, 13-, and 17-year-olds from 1977 and 1982 to 1986.

While most of the results presented here are based on responses to individual questions, others represent answers to sets of questions. A description of the analytic methods used to define composite variables across samples of students is provided in the Procedural Appendix.

Most of the tables in Part II—whether for 17-year-olds or eleventh graders—provide results for *all* high-school students who participated in the assessment and not just those currently enrolled in science classes. Students who were not taking a class at the time of the assessment were asked to answer the background questions based on the last time that they studied science. A comparative analysis revealed that on most items there was little difference between those currently enrolled in science classes and the entire sample. However, on items where differences were found, results are provided only for the sample of students enrolled in science courses at the time of the assessment, and these tables are marked accordingly.

Part II also contains information on teacher preparation and practice, gathered with a teacher questionnaire designed for the 1986 assessment. The questionnaire was distributed to a sample of the science teachers who were instructing students participating in each assessment session; thus, data from the questionnaire reflect the characteristics of assessed students' science teachers and are not representative of science teacher characteristics for the nation as a whole. (See Procedural Appendix for further information on the teacher questionnaire.)

CHAPTER 3
The Opportunity to Study Science

Exposure to Science Instruction

TTENTION HAS been drawn in recent years to the low amount of time devoted to science instruction in this country—particularly at the elementary school level—and to the equally critical issue of how that time is used. Recent international studies have heightened these concerns, as they document the limited course-taking experience and weak performance of American students in science relative to their peers abroad.[1] To assess recent patterns and trends in students' exposure to science instruction across the grades, NAEP asked students participating in the 1986 assessment and teachers responding to the new teacher questionnaire to report time spent on science teaching and learning.

Time Spent on Science Teaching and Learning: Grade 3

Teachers of assessed third-grade students were asked how much time they spent teaching science compared with carrying out other classroom activities. As shown in TABLE 3.1, approximately half the teachers at grade 3 reported spending one to two hours each week providing science instruction; meanwhile, only 5 percent reported spending five to six hours per week teaching science, and no teachers reported spending seven hours or more providing instruction. Approximately 10 percent of the teachers spent that amount of time maintaining order and discipline in the classroom.

... approximately half the teachers at grade 3 reported spending one to two hours each week providing science instruction; meanwhile, only 5 percent reported spending five to six hours per week teaching science...

---

[1]International Association for the Evaluation of Educational Achievement, *Science Achievement in 17 Countries: A Preliminary Report* (New York, NY: Teachers College, Columbia University, 1988).

TABLE 3.1

Grade 3
Uses of Time in the Classroom as Reported
by Assessed Students' Teachers, 1986*

How much time do you spend
on each of the following, with
a typical class during a
typical week?

Percent

Providing instruction in science.

None	6 (1.4)
Less than 1 hour	15 (1.8)
1 to 2 hours	49 (2.3)
3 to 4 hours	24 (2.2)
5 to 6 hours	5 (1.3)
7 or more hours	0 (0.2)

Maintaining order and disciplining students.

None	2 (0.8)
Less than 1 hour	54 (2.3)
1 to 2 hours	22 (2.1)
3 to 4 hours	5 (0.7)
5 to 6 hours	6 (1.3)
7 or more hours	11 (1.2)

Administering tests or quizzes, grading tests, in-class work, and homework.

None	0 (0.1)
Less than 1 hour	8 (1.3)
1 to 2 hours	26 (2.2)
3 to 4 hours	20 (1.7)
5 to 6 hours	13 (1.4)
7 or more hours	32 (1.8)

*Jackknifed standard errors are presented in parentheses.

These NAEP data generally appear to corroborate the findings of the *Report of the 1985-86 National Survey of Science and Mathematics Education*, in which elementary school teachers (K-3) reported spending an average of only 18 minutes per day teaching science—less than half the amount of time spent on mathematics instruction and one-quarter of the time given to reading instruction in these early grades.[2]

[2]Iris Weiss, *Report of the 1985-86 National Survey of Science and Mathematics Education* (Research Triangle Park, NC: Research Triangle Institute, 1987).

For comparison with teachers' estimates of the amount of time spent on teaching science, third-grade students were asked to report on the amount of time that they spent each week studying science in school. Although questions can be raised about the validity of their responses, third graders' reports appear to agree with those of their teachers on the small amount of class time devoted to science instruction. TABLE 3.2 presents the average science proficiency of third-grade students by their reported frequency of science lessons in 1986.

Grade 3: Average Science Proficiency by Frequency of Science Lessons, 1986*		TABLE 3.2
How often do you have a science lesson in school?	Percent	Proficiency
Never	11 (1.3)	198 (2.6)
Less than once each week	13 (1.2)	211 (3.0)
About once a week	23 (1.3)	216 (1.9)
Several times a week	25 (1.4)	219 (1.8)
Almost every day	27 (1.8)	211 (2.5)

*Jackknifed standard errors are presented in parentheses.

It is disturbing that 11 percent of the third graders reported never having a science lesson in school, and another 13 percent stated that they had science classes less than once each week. It appears that educators are justifiably concerned that American students in the early grades spend little time each week studying science.

Definitive statements cannot be made about the relationship between instructional exposure and proficiency at grade 3, given questions about the validity of these young students' responses. However, a generally positive relationship appears to exist between frequency of science lessons and science proficiency, with the exception of students reporting instruction almost every day. If these students are having a science lesson almost every day—and the observed relationship between frequency of instruction and proficiency is therefore accurate—it may be that frequent attention to the subject necessitates shorter lessons, reducing their effectiveness. At the other end of the spectrum, students who reported receiving no science instruction registered the lowest proficiency.

To measure the amount of time spent studying science outside of class time, third-grade students were asked to report how much science homework they did each week. TABLE 3.3 summarizes their responses.

It is disturbing that 11 percent of the third-graders reported never having a science lesson in school, and another 13 percent stated that they had science classes less than once each week.

Third graders appear to devote little time to science homework: Approximately two-thirds of the students at this grade level reported that they did less than a half-hour of this work each week. It is interesting to note that a negative relationship appears to exist between the amount of time that third-grade students spend on science homework and their science proficiency; that is, students who registered the highest proficiency reported doing no science homework. One might infer from the results that students who are having greater difficulty in science in this early grade are spending more time on homework.

Grade 3: Average Proficiency by Time Spent on Science Homework, 1986*		TABLE 3.3

About how much time do you usually spend on science homework each week?	Percent	Proficiency
No time	32 (1.2)	219 (2.2)
1/2-hour	36 (1.2)	217 (1.8)
1 hour	15 (0.8)	203 (3.2)
More than 1 hour	7 (0.6)	193 (4.1)

*Jackknifed standard errors are presented in parentheses. Percents do not total 100 due to the exclusion of students who were not receiving science instruction at the time of the assessment.

In summary, whether one views the amount of time spent on science teaching and learning through the eyes of the teacher or the student, it appears that there is relatively little science instruction provided to students in the early years of schooling. Unless greater measures are taken to strengthen elementary science instruction, it is unlikely that the problems of weak science proficiency and limited course-taking in the upper grades will be remedied.

Time Spent on Science Teaching and Learning: Grades 7 and 11

While educators have focused in recent years on the low amount and rigor of elementary-school science, perhaps as much or more concern has been voiced about students' lack of exposure to science instruction in the upper grades. This problem may be the result of inadequate course offerings, a declining supply of qualified science teachers, lenient graduation requirements, students' decisions not to enroll, or other variables; however, the relative influence of these variables is a question that remains unanswered.

Accordingly, NAEP asked the science teachers of seventh- and eleventh-grade students to report how much time they spent each week teaching science, and how much time they spent carrying out other classroom activities. TABLE 3.4 summarizes these responses.

Grades 7 and 11: Uses of Time in the Classroom as Reported by Assessed Students' Science Teachers, 1986*		TABLE 3.4

	Percentage of Teachers	
How much time do you spend on each of the following with a typical class during a typical week?	Grade 7	Grade 11
Providing instruction in science		
None	0 (0.0)	0 (0.0)
Less than 1 hour	1 (0.6)	2 (0.7)
1 hour	1 (0.8)	1 (0.4)
2 hours	15 (4.5)	7 (2.8)
3 hours	32 (3.4)	35 (3.1)
4 hours	37 (4.2)	42 (3.6)
5 hours or more	14 (3.8)	14 (2.5)
Maintaining order and disciplining students		
None	5 (1.9)	12 (2.5)
Less than 1 hour	72 (4.7)	76 (3.2)
1 hour	14 (3.7)	5 (1.6)
2 hours	6 (2.1)	4 (1.6)
3 hours	0 (0.0)	0 (0.4)
4 hours	1 (0.8)	3 (1.8)
5 hours or more	1 (0.7)	0 (0.4)
Administering tests or quizzes		
None	0 (0.3)	1 (0.4)
Less than 1 hour	44 (6.2)	40 (2.8)
1 hour	39 (6.6)	52 (3.4)
2 hours	10 (3.7)	6 (1.2)
3 hours	3 (1.3)	1 (0.4)
4 hours	2 (1.3)	0 (0.2)
5 hours or more	0 (0.2)	0 (0.0)

*Jackknifed standard errors are presented in parentheses.

Teachers of students at the seventh- and eleventh-grade levels appear to spend more time providing science instruction than administering tests or quizzes and maintaining order in the classroom. While this finding is encouraging, the amount of time spent teaching science still appears to be quite low: Approximately half of the teachers at grade 7 and 45 percent at grade 11 reported devoting three hours or less to science instruction each week. Only 14 percent of the teachers in either grade reported that they spent five hours or more each week actually teaching science.

As a measure of time spent studying science outside of school, students in the seventh and eleventh grades also were asked to report how much time they spent on science homework each week. TABLE 3.5 presents students' average proficiency scores by their responses to this question.

Grades 7 and 11: Average Proficiency by Time Spent on Science Homework, 1986*					TABLE 3.5

About how much time do you usually spend on science homework each week?	Grade 7		Grade 11	
	Percent	Proficiency	Percent	Proficiency
No time	16 (1.3)	243 (2.9)	12 (1.1)	285 (3.3)
Less than 1 hour	47 (1.3)	251 (1.4)	36 (2.0)	299 (2.5)
1-2 hours	26 (1.2)	250 (1.7)	31 (1.5)	304 (2.8)
3-4 hours	8 (1.1)	254 (3.9)	14 (1.5)	316 (4.3)
More than 4 hours	3 (0.4)	251 (4.1)	7 (0.7)	317 (5.4)

*Jackknifed standard errors are presented in parentheses.
Data for grade 11 represent only those students enrolled in a science class at the time of the assessment.

No consistent relationship appears to exist at the junior high-school level between homework and proficiency, although seventh-grade students who reported spending no time each week on science homework exhibited the lowest proficiency. At grade 11, the relationship between homework and science proficiency is consistently positive, with students who cited spending more than four hours each week on science homework registering the highest performance. At both grades 7 and 11, most students reported spending two hours or less on their homework each week, suggesting little time commitment to their science studies outside of school.

Science Curriculum: Grade 7

In addition to being disturbed by the low amount of science instruction across the grades, educators have voiced concern over the weak content and irregular sequence of science instruction. Many have criticized what is often referred to as the "layer-cake" approach to curriculum, in which students receive superficial instruction in a series of content areas, with little opportunity to integrate or deepen what they are learning. The NAEP data cannot address these criticisms; however, there does appear to be some variation in the focus of science instruction at the junior-high-school level. TABLE 3.6 provides data on the average science proficiency of seventh-grade students by the main curricular emphasis of their science instruction in 1986.

Grade 7: Average Science Proficiency by Emphasis of Science Instruction, 1986*

TABLE 3.6

What is the main thing you are studying in science class this year?	Percent	Proficiency
No Science	6 (1.1)	228 (4.0)
Life Science	45 (2.6)	252 (1.2)
Physical Science	9 (1.7)	250 (2.9)
Earth Science	10 (1.7)	249 (3.3)
General Science	24 (1.4)	258 (1.1)
Other Science	5 (0.4)	222 (2.2)

*Jackknifed standard errors are presented in parentheses.

It is of concern that six percent of the seventh-grade students were not taking a science class at the time of the assessment, as science course-taking is typically required until the middle years of high school. Those seventh graders who were taking a science class at the time of the assessment reported studying a range of content areas: Nearly half cited Life Science as the core of their instruction in 1986, and the remaining half cited a range of content areas, including General, Physical, Earth, and "other" sciences. A recent study on science education found that, in 1986, more than half of the junior high schools in this country offered courses in Life Science, Earth Science, and Physical Science, marking a shift from 1977, when General Science courses were the most commonly offered.[3]

It is of concern that six percent of the seventh-grade students were not taking a science class at the time of the assessment, as science course-taking is typically required until the middle years of high school.

---

[3]Iris Weiss, *Report of the 1985-86 National Survey of Science and Mathematics Education* (Research Triangle Park, NC: Research Triangle Institute, 1987).

The NAEP data reveal neither strong nor consistent relationships between curricular content and proficiency at grade 7, although students who were not taking a science class registered the lowest proficiency, and those who cited General Science as the major emphasis of their science instruction registered the highest proficiency. The latter finding may be expected, given that the assessment covers a range of topic areas, and students who are studying General Science have likely been exposed to a variety of these areas as part of their instruction.

Science Curriculum and Course-taking: Grade 11

The NAEP data indicate that many high-school students are not enrolled in science classes, whether because schools do not offer sufficient courses or because students choose not to enroll in them. TABLE 3.7 presents data on the average science proficiency of eleventh-grade students who were reportedly taking a science class at the time of the assessment, compared to those who were not.

Grade 11: Average Science Proficiency by Enrollment in a Science Class at the Time of the Assessment, 1986*		TABLE 3.7

Are you currently taking a class in science?	Percent	Proficiency
"Yes"	58 (1.2)	302 (1.3)
"No"	41 (1.2)	279 (1.2)

*Jackknifed standard errors are presented in parentheses.

Forty-one percent of the eleventh-grade students reported that they were not taking a science course at the time of the 1986 assessment, and their average proficiency was substantially lower than that of students who were enrolled in a science class at the time. It appears from the reports of both teachers and students that opportunities for in-school science learning are limited across the grades.

> It appears from the reports of both teachers and students that opportunities for in-school science learning are limited across the grades.

Students in the eleventh grade were also asked to report on the extent to which they had taken various science courses; responses to this question are summarized in TABLE 3.8.

Grade 11: Science Course-taking Patterns, 1986*		TABLE 3.8

	Percentage of Students	
How much have you studied the following subjects?	One year or more	Half year or less
General Science	71 (1.6)	29 (1.5)
Life Science	41 (2.0)	59 (1.9)
Biology	85 (1.6)	15 (1.3)
Environmental Science	16 (1.0)	84 (1.0)
Chemistry	37 (1.5)	63 (1.7)
Physical Science	41 (2.5)	59 (2.5)
Physics	8 (0.6)	92 (0.6)
Earth Science	38 (1.8)	62 (1.6)
Geology	5 (0.7)	95 (0.6)

*Jackknifed standard errors are presented in parentheses.

Course-taking patterns by grade 11 indicate some curricular variation. A majority of these high-school students reported that they had studied General Science or Biology for a year or more, and from one-third to one-half reported studying Life Science, Physical Science, Earth Science, or Chemistry for that amount of time. However, relatively few students in the eleventh grade reported having taken Physics or Geology for a year or more.

Course-taking patterns by grade 11 indicate some curricular variation.

Limited exposure to some of these courses may be unremarkable, given that Earth Science courses *per se* (including Geology) are relatively rare at the high-school level, and that Environmental Science and Biology may overlap with the Life Sciences. In addition, Physics is generally a twelfth-grade course, and eleventh-grade students would still have the opportunity to take the course in their senior year. Yet since Chemistry is commonly taught in the sophomore or junior year, it is of concern that 63 percent of the students in grade 11 reported that they had studied the subject for a half-year or less.

These course-taking patterns appear compatible with the preliminary findings of the 1987 High School Transcript Study, which analyzed the minimum credits earned by 1987 high-school graduates who had participated as eleventh-graders in the 1986 NAEP science assessment. The study found that while 90 percent of these graduating students had earned at least one academic credit (awarded for a full-year course) in Biology, far fewer had earned a credit in Chemistry (45 percent) or Physics (20 percent).[4] Eleventh-grade students' responses to course-taking questions were aggregated into a composite variable to determine to what extent their course-taking patterns followed the traditional sequence of Biology, Chemistry, and Physics. The results are summarized in TABLE 3.9.

Grade 11: Cumulative Science Course-taking, 1986*

TABLE 3.9

Courses Taken:	Percent	Proficiency
General Science only	9 (0.8)	263 (1.4)
Biology only	46 (1.3)	280 (0.8)
Biology + Chemistry	33 (1.2)	314 (0.9)
Biology + Chemistry + Physics	5 (0.4)	330 (2.5)

*Jackknifed standard errors are presented in parentheses.

This table does not include the 7 percent of grade 11 students whose course-taking did not match any of the categories presented here.

It cannot be determined from the data whether students who reported that they had only taken General Science had studied other courses not listed here, or whether these are students who were "tracked" into General Science based on their weak science proficiency in junior high school. Regardless, it is of concern that 10 percent of the eleventh graders had not completed Biology by their junior year.

Nearly half of these high-school students had completed only Biology, while one-third had taken both Biology and Chemistry. One might expect most students in eleventh grade to have progressed to Chemistry, but this does not appear to be the case. In addition, only 5 percent of the students reported having taken Physics in addition to these other three courses; however, they would still have the opportunity to take advanced courses in their senior year. These findings appear to be supported by preliminary data from the 1987 High School Transcript Study, which found that in 1987, 44 percent of graduating high-school students had taken Biology and Chemistry, and 17 percent had also completed a Physics course.[5]

As expected, a positive relationship appears to exist between the level of students' course-taking and their proficiency in the subject. While relatively

---

[4]Westat, Inc., Preliminary data from the 1987 High School Transcript Study prepared for the U.S. Department of Education, National Center for Education Statistics (March 1988).

[5]Westat, Inc., Preliminary data from the 1987 High School Transcript Study, prepared for the U.S. Department of Education, National Center for Education Statistics (March 1988).

few students had reached Physics, those who had done so registered the highest proficiency. At the other end of the spectrum, students who had only taken General Science exhibited lower average proficiency than students who had reached Biology, Chemistry, or Physics.

Trends in Curriculum and Course-taking: Age 17

It appears from the findings of the 1986 NAEP assessment and from other sources that many students—for reasons of access or choice—graduate from high school with relatively little exposure to advanced studies in science. However, an examination of trends from 1982 to 1986 reveals that high-school science course-taking has risen in recent years. TABLE 3.10 summarizes changes across time in the percentages of 17-year-old students who report having taken various courses.

Seventeen-year-olds were more likely in 1986 than in 1982 to report having studied at least one year of General Science, Life Science, Physical Science, or Earth Science, and as likely to report having taken at least one year of Biology, Chemistry, Physics, Geology, or Environmental Science. The NAEP trends in course-taking appear to be supported by results from the High School Transcript Study, which found that the mean number of full-year science courses taken by graduating high-school seniors had increased from 2.2 in 1982 to 2.6 in 1987, and that the percentage of high-school students earning minimum credits in science rose from 95 percent to 99 percent across that time span.[6] It seems plausible to infer that the current educational reform movement has played a role in these recent changes, with its efforts to raise the course-taking standards necessary for high-school graduation.

Summary

If this country is to strengthen its commitment to science education, a necessary part of that effort must be given to raising the level of high-school course-taking, which in turn requires that students in the earlier grades be more adequately prepared for advanced studies in the subject.

The NAEP data indicate that there are students across the grades who were not receiving *any* science instruction at the time of the 1986 assessment. Eleven percent of the third graders, 6 percent of the seventh graders, and 41 percent of the eleventh graders reported that they were not taking a science class in 1986.

[6]Westat, Inc., Preliminary data from the 1987 High School Transcript Study, prepared for the U.S. Department of Education, National Center for Education Statistics (March 1988).

. . . an examination of trends from 1982 to 1986 reveals that high-school science course-taking has risen in recent years.

Eleven percent of the third graders, 6 percent of the seventh graders, and 41 percent of the eleventh graders reported that they were not taking a science class in 1986.

Age 17: Trends in Science Course-taking Patterns, 1982-1986*

TABLE 3.10

How much have you studied the following subjects?	Percentage of Students	
	One year or more	Half year or less
GENERAL SCIENCE		
1982	61 (1.6)	39 (1.6)
1986	69 (1.6)	31 (1.5)
LIFE SCIENCE		
1982	27 (1.1)	73 (1.4)
1986	40 (2.0)	60 (2.0)
BIOLOGY		
1982	76 (1.7)	24 (1.4)
1986	80 (1.8)	20 (3.9)
ENVIRONMENTAL SCIENCE		
1982	13 (0.9)	87 (1.1)
1986	15 (1.2)	85 (1.1)
CHEMISTRY		
1982	30 (1.7)	70 (1.7)
1986	33 (1.7)	67 (1.9)
PHYSICAL SCIENCE		
1982	33 (2.1)	67 (1.5)
1986	41 (3.0)	59 (3.0)
PHYSICS		
1982	11 (0.9)	89 (1.0)
1986	10 (0.9)	90 (0.9)
EARTH SCIENCE		
1982	27 (1.9)	73 (1.7)
1986	38 (1.8)	62 (1.6)
GEOLOGY		
1982	4 (0.2)	96 (0.7)
1986	5 (0.6)	95 (0.6)

*Jackknifed standard errors are presented in parentheses.

A number of factors may contribute to this finding. In the early grades, science may not be seen as deserving the same level of curricular attention as reading or mathematics; studies have shown that more than twice as much time is devoted to these subjects in the elementary grades than is devoted to science instruction. At the upper grades, many students do not take upper-level science courses, particularly in the specialized disciplines of Chemistry and Physics.

For those students who are receiving science instruction across the grades, little class time appears to be given to the subject. Most teachers at the third-grade level reported spending two hours or less each week providing science instruction, while relatively more time was committed to maintaining order and disciplining students. Although teachers at the seventh- and eleventh-grade levels appear to spend more time teaching science than performing administrative and disciplinary functions, the amount of time spent on science instruction is still quite low. Only 14 percent of the teachers at grades 7 or 11 reported spending five hours or more each week teaching science.

Seventh-grade students who were taking a science class in 1986 reported studying several different content areas; while half reported Life Science as the focus of their science instruction that year, the other half reported a range of emphases, including General Science, Earth Science, and Physical Science. There appears to be no consistent relationship between the content of science instruction and proficiency at this grade level, although students studying General Science content registered slightly higher proficiency than students reporting other concentrations.

Assessment results from 1986 indicate that a majority of eleventh-grade students have taken Biology; however, 15 percent reported that they had studied the subject for less than a year or not at all. In addition, only slightly more than one-third of the eleventh-grade students stated that they had studied both Biology and Chemistry, and less than 10 percent had studied Biology, Chemistry, and Physics. Thus, many students appear to remain below expected levels of course-taking, based on the traditional curricular cluster of Biology, Chemistry, and Physics.

While these data suggest that students, on the average, receive too little exposure to science instruction, it is encouraging to find indications that high-school science course-taking has risen since 1982. Although questions of cause-and-effect cannot be answered by the NAEP data, a positive relationship appears to exist between course-taking and science proficiency. Recent increases in science course-taking at age 17 appear to correspond with improvements in the science proficiency of students at that age level across the two most recent assessments. It is hoped that continued efforts will be directed to broadening and deepening current educational reforms in an attempt to move the performance of the nation's high-school students—as well as those at the earlier grades—further along the road to academic recovery.

CHAPTER 4
The Impact of School Science

The Relationship Between Course-taking and Proficiency in Science Content Areas

T O FURTHER our understanding of science proficiency in the United States, this chapter examines students' performance in particular science content areas as well as the effects of course-taking on performance.[1] The topics covered in NAEP's 1986 science assessment were drawn from the major subdisciplines of science, as well as from areas cutting across these subdisciplines, including the nature of science and its history. This design permitted NAEP to compute results for five different science content-area subscales at grades 7 and 11: **Nature of Science, Life Sciences, Chemistry, Physics,** and **Earth and Space Sciences.** At grade 3, NAEP computed results for three content-area subscales—**Nature of Science, Life Sciences,** and **Physical Sciences** (combining basic Chemistry and Physics). A listing of the topics included in each science content-area subscale is presented in FIGURE 4.1.

The meaning of the science subscales cannot be known in absolute terms; that is, one cannot determine how much learning in Chemistry equals how much learning in the Life Sciences. However, the subscales do permit an analysis of the relative strengths and weaknesses of students in different grades or subgroups within each science content area.

---

[1]Because data on actual course-taking from the 1987 High School Transcript Study (discussed in Chapter 3) cannot be linked to proficiency data from the 1986 NAEP assessment, students' self-reported course-taking is used as the basis for the analyses presented in this chapter.

■ **Life Sciences (Biology)**
—Cellular and molecular biology
—Energy transformations (photosynthesis and cellular metabolism)
—Structure and functions of organisms (protists, plants, animals)
—Diversity of organisms (classification)
—Genetics and development
—Evolution
—Ecology
—Behavior

■ **Physics**
—Mechanics (motion, forces, principles of conservation)
—Waves and optics
—Electricity and magnetism
—Modern physics (atomic, nuclear, relativity)
—Heat and kinetic theory

■ **Chemistry**
—Structure of matter (nuclear, atomic, and molecular)
—Periodic classification
—States of matter and nature of solutions
—Reactions of matter (chemical transformations)
—Stoichiometry

■ **Earth and Space Sciences**
—The earth's history
—Materials of the earth
—Agents of processes of change in the earth's surface
—Earth's atmosphere and weather
—Describing and measuring time and location
—The oceans
—The solar system, galaxies, and the universe

■ **Nature of Science**
—Processes of science
—Assumptions of science
—Characteristics and limitations of scientific methods
—Ethics in science

NOTE: At grade 3, the Physics and Chemistry subscales were combined into a single Physical Sciences subscale.

---

[2]National Assessment of Educational Progress, *Science Objectives: 1985-86 Assessment* (Princeton, NJ: Educational Testing Service, 1987).

The subscaling methodology requires that each scale be anchored, or that some points be fixed. (Please refer to the Procedural Appendix for more detailed information on the scaling methodology.) Because the Nature of Science and Life Science subscales span all three grades, NAEP anchored each of these scales at grades 3 and 11, allowing the means to vary at grade 7.

A study of changes in average proficiency on the Life Sciences and Nature of Science subscales across the grades reveals some interesting findings, as shown in TABLE 4.1.

Grades 3, 7, and 11 Changes in Average Proficiency on the Life Sciences and Nature of Science Subscales Across the Grades, 1986*			TABLE 4.1

Subscale	Grade 3	Grade 7	Grade 11
Life Sciences	212 (0.9)	250 (0.8)	290 (1.0)
Nature of Science	213 (0.8)	247 (0.7)	292 (1.2)

*Jackknifed standard errors are presented in parentheses.

In the NAEP scaling metric, gains in average proficiency on the Life Sciences subscale were approximately the same from grades 3 to 7 and from grades 7 to 11—increases of 38 and 40 points, respectively. This indicates that students' understanding of the Life Sciences appears to grow steadily across the school years.

On the Nature of Science subscale, however, average proficiency tended to improve more between grades 7 and 11 (45 points) than between grades 3 and 7 (34 points). These findings suggest that curricular attention to fundamental aspects of the nature of science appears comparatively limited in elementary school.

Because three of the remaining subscales—Chemistry, Physics, and Earth and Space Sciences—were included only at grades 7 and 11, the national means for these subscales were necessarily anchored at these two grades. In addition, the Physical Sciences subscale was included only at grade 3. Therefore, the subscaling methodology does not permit an analysis of differences in students' average proficiency in these content areas across the grades.

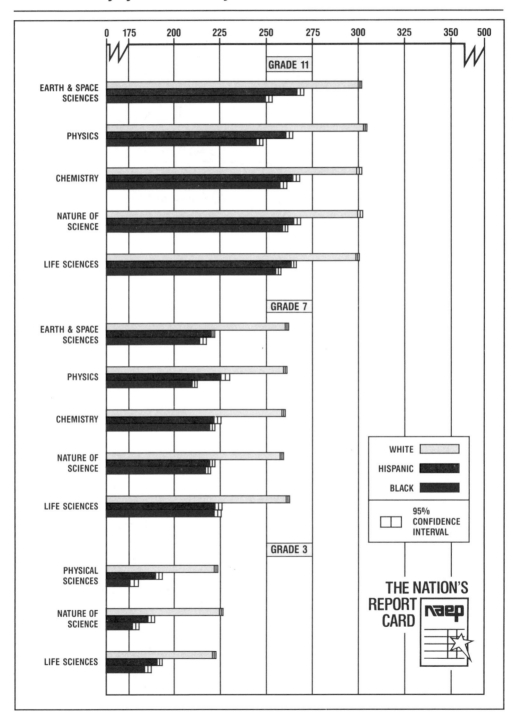

Science Content-Area Results by Race/Ethnicity

At grade 3, White students tended to have higher proficiency than Hispanic students and the latter group had higher proficiency than Black students on all three subscales—Nature of Science, Life Sciences, and Physical Sciences (FIGURE 4.2). This "stair-step" pattern of relative differences also occurred at grade 7, although there was little difference in performance between Hispanic and Black students on the Chemistry, Nature of Science, and Life Sciences subscales. A similar pattern was evident at grade 11 across all five science content areas, although White students performed relatively less well on the Life Sciences subscale at this grade level, and Black students performed less well on the Physics subscale.

As shown in TABLE 4.2, slightly fewer Hispanic eleventh graders than White or Black students reported having taken Biology.[3] In all three racial/ethnic groups, students who had taken the course performed much better on the Life Sciences subscale than those who had not. Similarly, students who reported having taken Chemistry performed substantially better on the Chemistry subscale than those who had not taken the course. Although many more White eleventh graders than Black or Hispanic eleventh graders reported having taken Chemistry, discrepancies in performance among racial/ethnic subgroups appeared similar for students who had taken the course compared to those who had not. As explained in Chapter 3, few students reported having taken Physics, likely because it is a twelfth-grade course; thus, the results are difficult to interpret. Generally, White students who reported Physics course-taking had much higher proficiency on the Physics subscale than those who had not taken the course, while proficiency levels seemed to be about the same for Black and Hispanic eleventh graders whether or not they reported having taken Physics.

Science Content-Area Results by Gender

Historically, fewer females than males have tended to do well in science or to pursue advanced studies and careers in science.[4] There is concern among science educators and within society at large that this discrepancy may result from a lack of sufficient academic support or from negative signals discouraging girls from developing their abilities in science.

---

[3]Although there appears to be high agreement between self-reported data on course-taking from the 1986 NAEP assessment and transcript data from 1987 High School Transcript Study, it should be cautioned that some students may over-report and others may under-report their course-taking experience. As a result, course-taking would appear to have less impact on proficiency than one might expect—or than actually occurs.

[4]Michael F. Crowley, *Women and Minorities in Science and Engineering* (Washington, DC: National Science Foundation, Division of Science Resources Studies, 1986).

TABLE 4.2

Grade 11: Average Proficiency Scores by Race/Ethnicity for the Life Sciences, Chemistry, and Physics Subscales by Course-taking in Related Subjects, 1986*

	Percent Having Taken Course	Proficiency Level Have Taken Course	Proficiency Level Have Not Taken Course
BIOLOGY			
White	89 (1.0)	302 (0.8)	276 (2.5)
Hispanic	82 (2.3)	269 (1.6)	248 (2.4)
Black	89 (1.3)	259 (1.7)	239 (3.0)
CHEMISTRY			
White	44 (1.4)	325 (1.0)	282 (1.2)
Hispanic	29 (2.9)	297 (2.7)	257 (2.1)
Black	31 (2.2)	289 (2.9)	247 (1.7)
PHYSICS			
White	10 (0.5)	331 (3.5)	300 (1.3)
Hispanic	15 (1.5)	261 (7.2)	264 (2.3)
Black	13 (1.1)	255 (5.9)	245 (2.1)

*Jackknifed standard errors are presented in parentheses.

As shown in FIGURE 4.3, the NAEP results lend weight to these concerns. Although there were no gender differences in performance at grade 3 on the Nature of Science and Life Sciences subscales, boys performed better than girls on the Physical Sciences subscale—an area related to basic mechanical principles. These results held for grade 7, with males performing better than females on the Chemistry, Physics, and Earth and Space Sciences subscales. Across the subscales, seventh-grade boys appeared relatively strong in Physics and relatively weak in the area of the Nature of Science, whereas girls performed similarly across the content areas with the exception of lower performance in Physics.

By grade 11, there were substantial gender differences in performance across most of the science content areas. While there were essentially no differences in performance between males and females on the Nature of Science subscale, the disparities noted at grade 7 on the Physics, Chemistry, and Earth and Space Sciences subscales tended to increase at grade 11, and a difference favoring males appeared on the Life Sciences subscale, as well. Across the five subscales, males performed comparatively better in the areas

By grade 11, there were substantial gender differences in performance across most of the science content areas.

of Chemistry, Physics, and Earth and Space Sciences, while females showed relatively weak performance in those areas, particularly in Physics.

What role does high-school course-taking play in these results? Do females simply take fewer science courses than males? TABLE 4.3 provides average proficiency levels on the Life Sciences, Chemistry, and Physics subscales for males and females who have taken Biology, Chemistry, or

---

Grades 3, 7, and 11: Science Content Area Proficiency by Gender, 1986

FIGURE 4.3

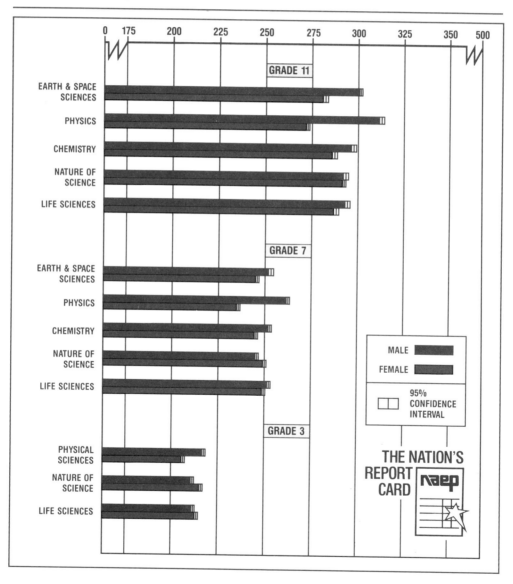

Physics courses. Most students in grade 11 have taken Biology, and it appears that just as many females as males (if not more) have taken the course. Students who had completed Biology performed significantly better on the Life Sciences subscale than those who had not, and the gender differences in performance remained essentially unchanged regardless of whether or not students had taken Biology.

	Percent Having Taken Course	Proficiency Level Have Taken Course	Proficiency Level Have Not Taken Course
Grade 11: Average Proficiency Scores by Gender for the Life Sciences, Chemistry, and Physics Subscales by Course-Taking in Related Subjects, 1986*			TABLE 4.3
BIOLOGY			
Male	88 (1.0)	298 (1.3)	271 (3.0)
Female	89 (0.9)	291 (0.9)	265 (2.5)
CHEMISTRY			
Male	44 (1.5)	325 (1.2)	279 (1.1)
Female	40 (1.5)	314 (1.5)	270 (1.1)
PHYSICS			
Male	13 (0.8)	335 (3.7)	311 (1.1)
Female	9 (0.6)	285 (3.4)	272 (1.3)

*Jackknifed standard errors are presented in parentheses.

Less than half of the students in grade 11 reported having taken Chemistry, with slightly more males than females having had the course. Unlike Biology, the gender gap increased among those students who had taken Chemistry, suggesting that Chemistry course-taking seemed to be much more beneficial for males. Very few students of either sex reported taking Physics although, as with Chemistry, slightly more males than females reported taking the course. A large gender gap existed for students who had not taken Physics and, although course-taking appeared to improve performance substantially for both males and females in this content area, it did nothing to reduce—and in fact may have increased—the difference in performance between them.

Very few students of either sex reported taking Physics although, as with Chemistry, slightly more males than females reported taking the course.

Science Content-Area Results by Region

Regional performance differences on the content-area subscales are presented in FIGURE 4.4. At grade 3, students from the Northeast and Central regions generally had higher proficiency than those from the West and Southeast on all three subscales. This generalization tended to hold across all five subscales at grade 7, while at grade 11, regional differences in performance were somewhat reduced. Although eleventh-grade students from the Northeast generally performed the best, followed by those from the Central, West, and Southeast regions in descending order, students from the Southeast did not lag behind in Chemistry as was evident in the other content areas. Across all subscales, the advantage held by Northeast students was minor, except on the Physics subscale, where students from this region performed particularly well.

The impact of course-taking on regional proficiency results can be seen in TABLE 4.4.

Although about the same percentage of eleventh-grade students from each region reported having taken Biology, substantially more students in the Northeast than in the other three regions reported having taken Chemistry and Physics. On the Life Sciences subscale, students from the Northeast and Central regions who had not taken Biology performed similarly, but students from the West and particularly the Southeast performed less well. In all four regions, eleventh graders who had taken Biology performed much better on the Life Sciences subscale than those who had not taken the course.

Among eleventh graders who had not taken Chemistry, those living in the Central region had a slight advantage and those living in the Southeast lagged behind in performance on the Chemistry subscale. For those eleventh graders who reported having taken the course, performance was similar for students in all four regions, with those in the Northeast and Central regions performing slightly better.

The regional impact of Physics course-taking is difficult to ascertain, because so few students reported having taken Physics that the measurement errors are quite large. For those students who had not taken a Physics course, proficiency was very similar on that subscale across regions except in the Southeast, where students had lower proficiency. It appears that Physics course-taking was related to improved performance on that subscale in three of the regions, the most notable of these being the Northeast. In contrast, students in the Southeast who reported having taken Physics did not seem to perform any better on that subscale than their classmates who had not taken the course.

FIGURE 4.4

Grades 3, 7, and 11: Science Content Area Proficiency by Region, 1986

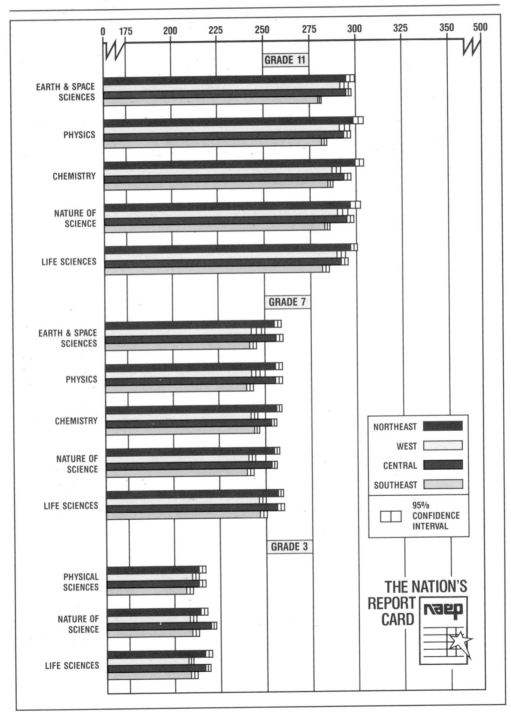

<table>
<tr><td colspan="2">Grade 11: Average Proficiency Scores by Region
for the Life Sciences, Chemistry, and Physics Subscales
by Course-Taking in Related Subjects, 1986*</td><td>TABLE 4.4</td></tr>
</table>

	Percent Having Taken Course	Proficiency Level Have Taken Course	Proficiency Level Have Not Taken Course
BIOLOGY			
Northeast	91 (1.7)	300 (1.9)	273 (5.2)
Central	86 (1.6)	296 (1.6)	273 (3.3)
West	87 (2.3)	294 (2.5)	266 (3.5)
Southeast	92 (0.8)	286 (1.5)	253 (3.8)
CHEMISTRY			
Northeast	57 (3.0)	323 (2.3)	274 (2.3)
Central	37 (2.7)	322 (1.8)	279 (1.7)
West	35 (2.6)	316 (3.4)	274 (1.8)
Southeast	40 (3.2)	315 (1.7)	270 (0.9)
PHYSICS			
Northeast	19 (1.6)	328 (4.9)	293 (3.0)
Central	8 (0.8)	315 (6.5)	293 (1.5)
West	10 (1.1)	305 (9.0)	291 (2.4)
Southeast	7 (0.8)	286 (6.0)	283 (1.5)

*Jackknifed standard errors are presented in parentheses.

Summary

The relationship between content-area proficiency and course-taking appears to be a complex one. White students had higher proficiency levels in each science content area than did Hispanic students, and Hispanic students tended to have higher proficiency than Black students. White students did not report taking more courses in these content areas, except in Chemistry. Students in all three racial/ethnic groups who reported taking Biology did much better on the Life Sciences subscale than those who had not taken the course, just as those who reported having taken Chemistry did much better on that subscale. In contrast, only the performance of White students appeared to improve as a result of Physics course-taking; Black and Hispanic eleventh graders who reported having taken Physics did no better on that

89

subscale than their classmates who reported not having taken the course. By grade 11, White students' performance in the area of Life Sciences appeared to be relatively weak compared to their performance in other content areas, and Black students' performance appeared to be comparatively weak in Physics. Eleventh-grade Hispanic students had similar proficiency levels across all five science content areas.

Females performed as well as males in the Nature of Science content area at all three grade levels, and in the Life Sciences content area until the eleventh grade. However, the gender discrepancies in performance on the Physical Sciences subscale were substantial at all three grade levels. Somewhat fewer females than males reported having taken Chemistry and Physics classes, and both genders show improved performance with course-taking; however, the differences in performance between the sexes do not appear to be lessened by taking these courses, and in fact, seem to increase.

In the lower grades, students from the Northeast and Central regions had generally higher proficiency than those from the West and Southeast on all science content-area subscales. At grade 11, students from the Northeast tended to have the highest proficiency, followed by those from the Central, the West, and finally the Southeast regions. In the Northeast, students who had taken science courses performed comparatively better on the Life Sciences, Chemistry, and Physics subscales than those who had not taken these courses. This was also true for students from the Southeast in performance on the Life Sciences and Chemistry subscales, but not on the Physics subscale. More students from the Northeast than from other regions reported taking specialized science courses, and the courses they took appeared to be comparatively more effective in raising proficiency.

The NAEP data indicate a positive relationship between science course-taking and proficiency in the subject, although the nature of this relationship is unknown. Brighter students may take more science courses; alternatively, science course-taking may improve students' proficiency. In either case, the relationship between course-taking and proficiency appears to be stronger for certain subgroups and in certain content areas than for others. In situations where course-taking appears to have little or no relationship to performance, unexamined factors may be affecting the results. For example, when a student reports that he or she has taken a course, the depth or breadth of instruction may be different from the same course taken by other students. Thus the data must be viewed with sensitivity to the variety of factors that may influence the relationship between course-taking and content-area proficiency.

CHAPTER 5
The Nature of School Science

Teacher Qualifications and Classroom Practices

I N RECENT years, educators and policy makers have viewed many facets of science education with a critical eye—including not only the quantity and content of instruction as discussed in Chapters 3 and 4, but also instructional practices and teacher qualifications.[1] This chapter of the report addresses the latter two areas, contributing to the growing body of information on the profession and practice of science teaching and the relationship of certain instructional approaches to science proficiency.

Teaching Certification

Teachers of students assessed in grades 3, 7, and 11 were asked whether they had certification to teach science from the state in which they taught, and if so, to describe the nature of their certification. In addition, teachers were asked to report the highest academic degree they had received. Responses to these questions are presented in TABLE 5.1.

As expected, the science teachers of students assessed in grade 11 were more likely to be certified to teach science and to have advanced academic degrees than were teachers at the lower grades. Nearly all third-grade teachers reported being certified to teach elementary education, while only 7 percent had general science certification. At grade 7, most teachers were

... the science teachers of students assessed in grade 11 were more likely to be certified to teach science and to have advanced academic degrees than were teachers at the lower grades.

---

[1]The data on teacher qualifications and practices reported in this chapter represent all teachers at grade 3, and science teachers only at grades 7 and 11.

TABLE 5.1

Grades 3, 7, and 11
Certification and Academic Training
of Students' Science Teachers, 1986*

	Percent Responding "Yes"		
Do you have teaching certification from the state where you teach in any of the following areas?†	**Grade 3**	**Grade 7**	**Grade 11**
Elementary education	95 (1.2)	47 (4.0)	—
Middle or junior high school	38 (2.9)	84 (3.5)	60 (5.1)
Science (general certification)	7 (1.3)	63 (4.7)	80 (2.9)
What type of teaching certification do you have from the state where you teach?			
Not certified	2 (0.5)	1 (0.9)	3 (1.4)
Temporary or provisional	4 (1.1)	7 (2.6)	5 (2.0)
Regular certification	27 (2.8)	39 (4.9)	26 (2.9)
Highest certification offered	66 (3.0)	53 (5.1)	66 (3.4)
What is the highest academic degree you hold?			
Bachelor's degree	61 (2.8)	57 (4.6)	44 (2.8)
Master's degree	36 (2.9)	36 (4.6)	46 (3.2)
Professional diploma	2 (0.8)	6 (2.5)	6 (2.4)
Doctorate	0 (0.0)	0 (0.4)	3 (2.0)

*Jackknifed standard errors are presented in parentheses. Data is provided only for teachers who responded to these questions. Due to a high rate of non-response (10-20 percent), standard errors for these items may be poorly estimated.

†Figures total to more than 100, as teachers may be certified in more than one area.

certified to teach middle or junior high school (84 percent) while fewer were certified to teach broad field science (63 percent); by comparison, 80 percent of the eleventh-grade teachers had General Science certification.

More than half of the assessed students' teachers at each grade level stated that they possessed the highest certification awarded by the state in which they taught, although seventh-grade teachers were less likely than third- or eleventh-grade teachers to be certified at the highest level. Given concern about the supply of qualified science instructors in American schools, particularly in the upper grades, the generally high levels of certification reported by students' teachers may be viewed as a positive sign.

... the generally high levels of certification reported by students' teachers may be viewed as a positive sign.

The science teachers participating in the survey also appeared to be well-educated, with academic credentials increasing across the grades. Although the highest level of education attained by most third- and seventh-grade teachers was the bachelor's degree, more than one-third of the teachers in both grades had also completed a master's degree. Of the participating eleventh-grade teachers, nearly half reported having a master's degree, and 9 percent had gone on to complete either a professional degree or doctorate. Although they are based on different samples of teachers and different questions, these data generally agree with the findings of other research on teacher qualifications.[2]

Years of Teaching Experience

As a measure of their teaching experience, seventh- and eleventh-grade teachers were asked to report how long they had been teaching science. Their responses are presented in TABLE 5.2.

Grades 7 and 11 Years of Teaching Experience Reported by Students' Science Teachers, 1986*		TABLE 5.2

How long have you been teaching science?	Percentage of Teachers	
	Grade 7	Grade 11
0-4 years	22 (3.9)	17 (3.2)
5-9 years	21 (4.7)	20 (2.5)
10-14 years	15 (3.1)	20 (2.9)
15-19 years	24 (4.2)	13 (2.0)
20+ years	18 (4.5)	30 (2.9)
Average number of years	12	14

*Jackknifed standard errors are presented in parentheses.

The distribution of years of teaching experience was quite similar across the two upper grades, although the average number of years of teaching experience was slightly higher for teachers of eleventh-grade students than for teachers of seventh-grade students. Nearly one-third of the eleventh-grade teachers and slightly less than one-fifth of those at the seventh-grade

[2]Iris Weiss, *Report of the 1985-86 National Survey of Science and Mathematics Education* (Research Triangle Park, NC: Research Triangle Institute, 1987).

level were what might be referred to as "veteran" science teachers, with more than 20 years of experience in teaching the subject. At the other end of the spectrum, there were slightly more "novice" teachers—those with less than 5 years of experience—at grade 7 than at grade 11. These findings appear to support data on teaching experience cited in recent literature on science education.[3]

Self-Perceived Preparation for Teaching Science

Although all of the teachers in the sample had been teaching science, as shown in TABLE 5.3, there were some differences across the grades in the percentages of teachers who felt adequately prepared to do so.

Grades 3, 7, and 11 Percentage of Students' Science Teachers Who Felt Prepared to Teach Science, 1986*			TABLE 5.3
	Percent Responding "Yes"		
	Grade 3	Grade 7	Grade 11
Do you feel adequately prepared to teach physical or natural science?	80 (2.0)	95 (1.7)	97 (1.1)

*Jackknifed standard errors are presented in parentheses.

Although most teachers across the grades reported that they felt adequately prepared to teach science, those at the upper grades were more likely than those at grade 3 to report feeling this way. This finding is perhaps explained by the fact that respondents in grades 7 and 11 were science teachers, whereas those in grade 3 were teachers for all subjects, and therefore unlikely to have the same depth of experience in science instruction as teachers in the upper grades.

Grouping Students for Instruction

To discern how much time teachers spend presenting material to the whole class versus working with students individually and in small groups,

---

[3]Iris Weiss, *Report of the 1985-86 National Survey of Science and Mathematics Education* (Research Triangle Park, NC: Research Triangle Institute, 1987).

the teacher questionnaire asked respondents to note the amount of time spent teaching in different groupings of students within the classroom. Responses are provided in TABLE 5.4.

| Grades 7 and 11: Grouping Students in the Science Classroom as Reported by Students' Science Teachers, 1986* | TABLE 5.4 |

How much time do you spend on each of the following, with a typical class during a typical week?	Percent of Teachers	
	Grade 7	Grade 11
Leading an activity for the whole class		
None	0 (0.3)	1 (0.6)
Less than 1 hour	4 (1.7)	3 (0.9)
1 hour	16 (3.6)	11 (2.4)
2 hours	23 (3.8)	23 (2.8)
3 hours	28 (5.1)	33 (3.1)
4 hours	17 (3.7)	17 (2.9)
5 or more hours	12 (3.0)	11 (1.9)
Working with a small group of students		
None	8 (2.9)	4 (1.2)
Less than 1 hour	37 (4.2)	28 (2.7)
1 hour	22 (4.2)	43 (4.2)
2 hours	20 (2.9)	18 (2.6)
3 hours	4 (1.5)	3 (0.9)
4 hours	6 (2.9)	2 (0.9)
5 or more hours	1 (0.5)	1 (0.5)
Working with individual students		
None	1 (0.5)	3 (1.7)
Less than 1 hour	38 (5.4)	31 (2.7)
1 hour	34 (5.3)	42 (4.3)
2 hours	15 (3.1)	18 (3.4)
3 hours	6 (1.7)	4 (1.1)
4 hours	3 (1.2)	0 (0.4)
5 or more hours	3 (1.4)	2 (0.7)

*Jackknifed standard errors are presented in parentheses.

The science teachers of students assessed in grades 7 and 11 reported spending more time leading activities for the whole class than working with individuals or small groups within the class. Nearly half of the teachers at grade 7 and approximately one-third at grade 11 reported spending less than an hour each week working with small groups of students. There appeared to be few differences between the grades in the amount of time that teachers spent each week working with any of these instructional groupings.

Access to Laboratory Facilities

Laboratory experimentation and other hands-on activities are thought by most educators to be an integral part of science learning, as they enable students to study the subject in a manner consistent with the practice of science.[4] Unfortunately, many science teachers at the seventh- and eleventh-grade levels responded that they had no laboratory facilities available for these kinds of activities, as shown in TABLE 5.5.

Grades 7 and 11: Access to Laboratory Facilities as Reported by Students' Science Teachers, 1986*		TABLE 5.5

	Percent Responding "Yes"	
	Grade 7	Grade 11
Do you have access to a general purpose science laboratory for your teaching?	46 (6.0)	45 (4.3)
Do you have access to a specialized science laboratory for your teaching?	20 (4.6)	64 (3.5)

*Jackknifed standard errors are presented in parentheses.

Slightly less than half of the teachers in either grade reported that they had access to a general purpose laboratory for use in teaching science, and less than one-fifth of the seventh-grade teachers had access to more specialized facilities (i.e., a Biology or Chemistry laboratory). Almost two-thirds of the grade 11 teachers had access to a specialized laboratory. Without access to laboratory facilities, it is perhaps not surprising that so few of our students understand the tools and methods of science.

Without access to laboratory facilities, it is perhaps not surprising that so few of our students understand the tools and methods of science.

[4]Wayne W. Welch, "A Science-Based Approach to Science Learning," in *Research Within Reach*, eds. David Holdzkom and Pamela Lutz (Washington, DC: National Science Teachers Association, 1984).

Instructional Activities

To broaden the view of science instruction provided by teachers, students participating in the 1986 assessment were asked to describe their science courses in terms of instructional practices and curricular activities. NAEP was interested in determining to what extent students learned science through teacher lectures and demonstrations, compared to how frequently they engaged in "doing science," discussing the results of experiments, hypothesizing, and interpreting data. Students also were asked to report how often they solved science problems, conducted experiments alone or with other students, wrote up the results of experiments, read articles on science, and presented oral or written reports.

Responses to these questions were combined in a background indicator that classified the extent to which instructional activities were innovative, challenging, and participatory; three levels were defined, and labeled "low," "medium," and "high." Students whose teachers often lectured and seldom engaged the class in experimentation and other activities were clustered at the low end of the scale; in contrast, those whose teachers encouraged more innovative activities such as hypothesis-testing, doing hands-on work, and discussing experimental results were grouped at the high end of the scale. (See the Procedural Appendix for a discussion of the methods used to form background indicators.)

... seventh- and eleventh-grade students who reported classroom activities that were challenging and participatory were likely to have higher science proficiency.

As shown in FIGURE 5.1, seventh- and eleventh-grade students who reported classroom activities that were challenging and participatory were likely to have higher science proficiency.

Although it is not possible to determine whether students with greater science proficiency tend to be in classes that consist of more innovative curricular activities—or whether these activities yield higher proficiency—the positive relationship observed between the two is worth emphasizing. Further research is needed to address the more intricate questions of cause and effect that are presented by these data.

Although a positive relationship was evident between science proficiency and innovative instructional activities, a closer examination of the data reveals that these activities are relatively rare. TABLE 5.6 displays the relative frequency of various teaching practices reported in 1986 by students in grades 7 and 11.

Eleventh-grade students were more likely than seventh-graders to report that their teachers lectured on a daily basis, although this mode of instruction predominated at both grade levels. Other teaching practices were reported less frequently; in particular, it is disappointing that approximately half of the seventh-grade students and nearly one-quarter of the eleventh-

Average Science Proficiency by Types of
Teaching Practices and Instructional Activities, 1986 *

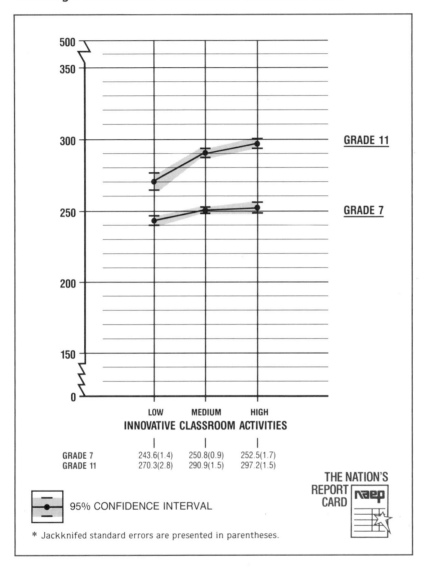

	LOW	MEDIUM	HIGH
GRADE 7	243.6(1.4)	250.8(0.9)	252.5(1.7)
GRADE 11	270.3(2.8)	290.9(1.5)	297.2(1.5)

95% CONFIDENCE INTERVAL

THE NATION'S
REPORT
CARD naep

* Jackknifed standard errors are presented in parentheses.

grade students reported never being asked to suggest hypotheses or interpret data—two fundamental skills in science.

In addition to describing their teachers' instructional methods, students in all three grades were asked to report on the kinds of learning activities featured in their science classes, ranging from doing reports and experiments

Grades 7 and 11	TABLE 5.6
Teaching Practices in Science, 1986*	

In your science class how often does your teacher do each of the following?	Daily	Several Times a Week	Once a Week	Less than Once a Week	Never
Grade 7					
Lecture	31 (0.9)	21 (0.9)	18 (1.1)	13 (0.9)	18 (0.9)
Demonstrate a scientific principle	15 (1.0)	22 (1.3)	22 (1.0)	22 (1.3)	19 (0.9)
Ask for reasons for the results of experiments	14 (1.1)	19 (1.3)	20 (0.8)	24 (1.1)	23 (1.0)
Ask you to suggest hypotheses	8 (0.8)	12 (0.8)	15 (1.0)	24 (1.0)	42 (1.5)
Ask you to interpret data	9 (0.9)	12 (0.7)	15 (0.7)	15 (1.0)	48 (1.2)
Grade 11					
Lecture	55 (1.0)	24 (0.8)	9 (0.8)	3 (0.3)	8 (0.7)
Demonstrate a scientific principle	18 (1.0)	31 (1.6)	28 (1.2)	13 (1.0)	10 (0.7)
Ask for reasons for the results of experiments	16 (1.1)	29 (0.9)	28 (1.0)	15 (0.9)	12 (0.8)
Ask you to suggest hypotheses	11 (0.7)	19 (0.8)	23 (1.3)	22 (1.0)	25 (1.3)
Ask you to interpret data	15 (0.8)	24 (0.9)	23 (0.9)	16 (0.9)	22 (1.0)

*Jackknifed standard errors are presented in parentheses.

to watching films, reading textbooks, and using other resources. Responses are summarized in TABLE 5.7.

The instructional activity reported most often by students was reading science textbooks; over half of the students at all three grades stated that they read textbooks daily or weekly, while most other kinds of learning opportunities are neglected. At least one-half of the students in third grade reportedly never went on field trips with their science classes—thus missing a potentially rich source of learning in the early grades. One-half or more of the students in grade 7 reported that they never conducted independent science experiments, wrote up the results of experiments, or went on science field trips. Approximately half responded that they never did oral or written reports for science class.

<table>
<tr><td colspan="2">Grades 3, 7, and 11
Frequency of Selected Instructional Activities, 1986*</td><td>TABLE 5.7</td></tr>
</table>

In science class, how often do you do each of the following?	Daily	Weekly	Monthly	Yearly	Never
Grade 3					
Watch a film.	—	23 (1.8)	16 (0.9)	18 (1.3)	31 (1.3)
Go on a field trip.	—	3 (0.5)	7 (0.6)	24 (1.1)	55 (1.7)
Do experiments.	11 (1.0)	30 (1.4)	—	26 (1.0)	19 (1.4)
Read your science textbook.	33 (1.7)	27 (1.5)	—	11 (0.7)	15 (0.8)
Do an oral or a written report.	20 (0.9)	16 (0.9)	—	17 (0.9)	33 (1.4)

	Daily	Several Times a Week	Once a Week	Less than Once a Week	Never
Grade 7					
Watch a film.	4 (0.7)	11 (1.0)	23 (1.4)	40 (1.7)	21 (1.4)
Go on a field trip.	1 (0.2)	1 (0.2)	1 (0.3)	16 (1.5)	82 (1.5)
Do experiments alone.	3 (0.5)	5 (0.5)	13 (0.9)	29 (1.0)	50 (1.4)
Do experiments with other students.	4 (0.5)	9 (0.7)	22 (1.4)	34 (1.5)	30 (1.3)
Write up experiments.	4 (0.6)	5 (0.5)	10 (1.1)	21 (1.3)	60 (1.6)
Read your science textbook.	43 (1.7)	24 (1.2)	15 (0.8)	8 (0.9)	9 (0.9)
Read articles on science.	12 (1.1)	14 (0.8)	23 (1.3)	25 (1.1)	26 (1.3)
Do an oral or a written report.	3 (0.4)	5 (0.5)	11 (0.9)	35 (1.9)	46 (1.9)
Grade 11					
Watch a film.	2 (0.2)	7 (0.6)	22 (1.2)	42 (1.2)	27 (1.1)
Go on a field trip.	0 (0.2)	0 (0.1)	1 (0.4)	13 (1.2)	86 (1.2)
Do experiments alone.	2 (0.3)	7 (0.6)	20 (0.9)	25 (1.0)	46 (1.3)
Do experiments with other students.	3 (0.6)	14 (0.9)	36 (1.2)	28 (1.4)	18 (1.4)
Write up experiments.	2 (0.3)	10 (0.9)	22 (1.3)	24 (1.5)	41 (1.6)
Read your science textbook.	28 (1.0)	26 (1.0)	16 (0.9)	12 (0.8)	18 (1.3)
Read articles on science.	7 (0.7)	10 (0.8)	18 (1.1)	26 (1.1)	39 (1.5)
Do an oral or a written report.	2 (0.3)	3 (0.3)	10 (0.8)	34 (1.3)	52 (1.6)

*Jackknifed standard errors are presented in parentheses.

[—] Response option not included. Percents at grade 3 do not total 100 due to the exclusion of students not receiving science instruction at the time of the assessment.

... the NAEP data indicate that many students do not engage in writing activities ... as part of their science instruction.

Similarly, nearly one-half of the eleventh-grade students reported never working independently on or writing up results from science experiments, and slightly more reported never doing oral or written reports. Despite the belief of many educators that writing should be integrated across the curriculum, the NAEP data indicate that many students do not engage in writing activities of the types mentioned as part of their science instruction.

An additional question not reported here asked students in each grade to report the number of science experiments that they had conducted in the previous month. Approximately half (49 percent) of the students in grade 11 reported that they had performed no experiments, while 44 percent in grade 7 and 40 percent in grade 3 reported no experiments. These findings give serious cause for concern, as experimentation and the thinking skills it entails are an integral part of the practice of science.

Summary

Less than half of the teachers of students assessed in 1986 reported that they had access to a general purpose laboratory for use in science instruction, thus reducing students' opportunities to engage in "doing" science.

Data from the teacher questionnaire indicate that at all three grades, most of the science teachers of students assessed in 1986 were reportedly certified to teach science and held at least regular teaching certification from the states in which they taught; many also possessed advanced academic degrees. More than half of the responding teachers had been teaching science for 10 or more years, and a majority at all three grades reported feeling well qualified to teach science.

Data on instructional practices from the 1986 science assessment suggest a continuation of several themes from the past. While innovative instructional approaches appear to be related to science proficiency, and many science educators encourage the use of hands-on activities, responses from students in all three grades indicate that science instruction continues to be dominated by teacher lectures and textbooks. Meanwhile, activities such as experimentation and use of scientific equipment remain comparatively rare. Less than half of the teachers of students assessed in 1986 reported that they had access to a general purpose laboratory for use in science instruction, thus reducing students' opportunities to engage in "doing" science.

Part III
The Unscientific Americans?

Experiential, Home, and Attitudinal Factors Associated with Science Learning

... out-of-school activities offer a range of different opportunities for science learning, providing for the kinds of informal education that arise from life experiences.

S CHOOL SCIENCE provides students the opportunity to gain scientific knowledge and understanding and to apply their skills in structured problem settings. Yet out-of-school activities offer a range of different opportunities for science learning, providing for the kinds of informal education that arise from life experiences. Students' independent explorations of natural phenomena, their uses of scientific equipment for practical purposes, involvement in science-related hobbies, home participation in science projects and activities, and other out-of-school experiences are thought to influence science learning; however, further research is needed to determine more precisely the influence of these activities on science proficiency.

The chapters in Part III of this report explore students' exposure to out-of-school opportunities for science learning and articulate the relationship between home, personal, and experiential variables and science proficiency. Chapter 6 describes students' experience using the tools of science—from basic scientific equipment to more sophisticated apparatus—and efforts to apply their science knowledge and understandings to various hands-on tasks. Chapter 7 addresses the home context for science learning, providing information on the availability of educational materials in the home and the amount of television viewing reported by students, as well as the extent of home involvement in science homework, projects, and activities. Chapter 8 summarizes students' perceptions of the utility and relevance of science learning, and their views on the applications of scientific knowledge to particular national and international problems.

Assessment Procedures

Background questions on independent experiences, home variables, and attitudes discussed in Part III were administered to students according to the procedures described in the introduction to Part II of this report. While most of the results are based on responses to individual questions, others represent answers to sets of questions. A description of the analytic methods used to define composite variables across samples of students is provided in the Procedural Appendix.

CHAPTER 6
Using the Tools of Science

Independent Experiences in Science Learning

Students . . . were asked to report on their use of various tools of science and their involvement in science-related activities . . .

I N THIS chapter, attention is given to the more informal and everyday opportunities for science learning and to the ways in which students' interest and proficiency in science may be related to these independent experiences. Students participating in the 1986 assessment were asked to report on their use of various tools of science and their involvement in science-related activities as indicators of their out-of-school learning.

Use of Scientific Equipment

Third- and seventh-grade students were asked to report the kinds of scientific equipment with which they had experience. Students in grade 3 were asked whether they had ever used a meter stick, a scale to weigh things, a magnifying glass, a thermometer, a yardstick, and a calculator. In grade 7, many of the pieces of equipment listed were more sophisticated and specific to in-school science learning; these junior high-school students were asked whether they had experience using a telescope, microscope, barometer, or a meter to measure electricity.

A background indicator was constructed to provide a general measure of third- and seventh-grade students' reported use of scientific equipment. FIGURE 6.1 displays the relationship between students' levels of experience using various kinds of equipment and their average science proficiency. Students who had used a number of different types of equipment were grouped at the high end of the scale, while those who had used few of the types of apparatus listed were grouped at the low end of the scale.

Grades 3 and 7
Average Science Proficiency
by Use of Science Equipment, 1986*

FIGURE 6.1

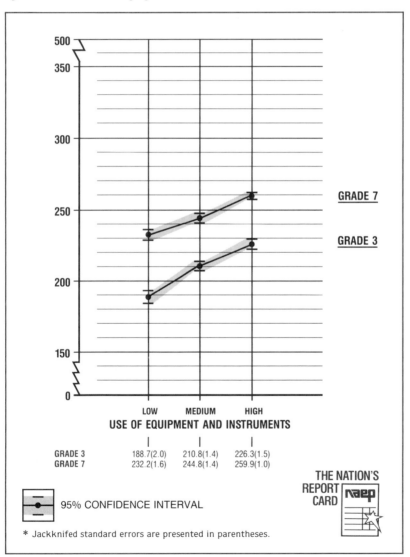

USE OF EQUIPMENT AND INSTRUMENTS

	LOW	MEDIUM	HIGH
GRADE 3	188.7(2.0)	210.8(1.4)	226.3(1.5)
GRADE 7	232.2(1.6)	244.8(1.4)	259.9(1.0)

THE NATION'S
REPORT
CARD

95% CONFIDENCE INTERVAL

* Jackknifed standard errors are presented in parentheses.

It appears that a positive relationship exists at grades 3 and 7 between students' experience using various kinds of scientific equipment and their science proficiency, although the causality of this relationship is unknown. Students with higher science proficiency may use more scientific equipment as a result of their greater facility or involvement in the subject, or their enrollment in resource-rich schools; alternatively, students who use more scientific equipment may have higher proficiency in part as a result of these experiences. In either case, the use of scientific equipment appears to be correlated with science achievement, and the curricular implications of this finding deserve further exploration.

Use of Scientific Equipment by Demographic Subgroups

Some interesting differences in students' reported use of scientific equipment were evident in an analysis of the results by race/ethnicity and by gender. FIGURE 6.2 displays the extent to which third-grade students in various demographic subgroups reported using such basic scientific equipment as yardsticks, scales, and magnifying glasses, as well as more sophisticated equipment, such as microscopes and telescopes.

While most students at this grade reported having had experience with basic scientific equipment, less than half had used the more sophisticated instruments listed. White students in grade 3 were consistently more likely to report having used various scientific apparatus than were Black and Hispanic students, whose experience appeared to be highly similar. It is interesting to note that the greatest discrepancies between White students' and Black and Hispanic students' use of equipment occurred primarily in experience with less sophisticated devices, such as yardsticks, scales, and magnifying glasses. Use of more sophisticated equipment was less skewed across racial/ethnic subpopulations.

In contrast to the results by race/ethnicity, roughly the same percentages of males and females in grade 3 reported having used basic scientific equipment (e.g., yardsticks, scales to weigh things, or magnifying glasses). However, a smaller percentage of third-grade girls than boys—some 14 percent less—had experience with more advanced apparatus (e.g., a microscope or telescope). It appears that even in this early grade, boys have greater experience with these tools of science.

Seventh- and eleventh-grade students were also asked to report on their experience using microscopes and telescopes in addition to other kinds of scientific equipment. Responses for the nation and selected demographic subgroups are presented in FIGURES 6.3A and 6.3B.

... the greatest discrepancies between White students' and Black and Hispanic students' use of equipment occurred primarily in experience with less sophisticated devices, such as yardsticks, scales, and magnifying glasses.

107

Grade 3: Experience with
Science Equipment for the Nation
and Selected Subgroups, 1986*

FIGURE 6.2

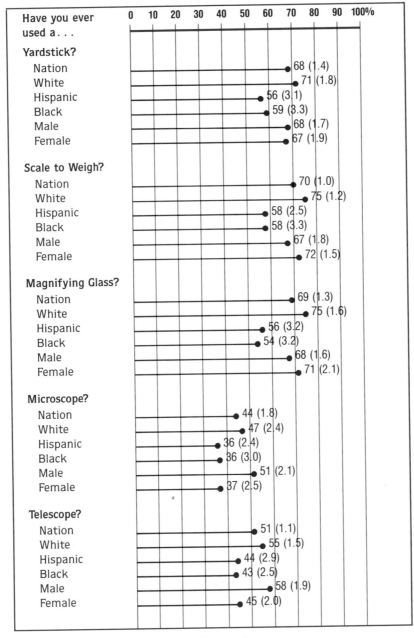

Percent Responding "Yes"

Have you ever used a...	Percent
Yardstick?	
Nation	68 (1.4)
White	71 (1.8)
Hispanic	56 (3.1)
Black	59 (3.3)
Male	68 (1.7)
Female	67 (1.9)
Scale to Weigh?	
Nation	70 (1.0)
White	75 (1.2)
Hispanic	58 (2.5)
Black	58 (3.3)
Male	67 (1.8)
Female	72 (1.5)
Magnifying Glass?	
Nation	69 (1.3)
White	75 (1.6)
Hispanic	56 (3.2)
Black	54 (3.2)
Male	68 (1.6)
Female	71 (2.1)
Microscope?	
Nation	44 (1.8)
White	47 (2.4)
Hispanic	36 (2.4)
Black	36 (3.0)
Male	51 (2.1)
Female	37 (2.5)
Telescope?	
Nation	51 (1.1)
White	55 (1.5)
Hispanic	44 (2.9)
Black	43 (2.5)
Male	58 (1.9)
Female	45 (2.0)

* Jackknifed standard errors presented in parentheses.

THE NATION'S
REPORT
CARD

naep

108

In grades 7 and 11, students' reported use of various types of scientific equipment continued to climb, although it increased for some subpopulations more than others. With a few slight exceptions, Black and Hispanic students in the seventh grade were less likely than their White peers to report experience using any of the types of equipment listed. While the gender difference in experience with microscopes appears to vanish by the seventh

Grade 7: Experience with Science Equipment for the Nation and Selected Subgroups, 1986*

FIGURE 6.3A

Percent Responding "Yes"

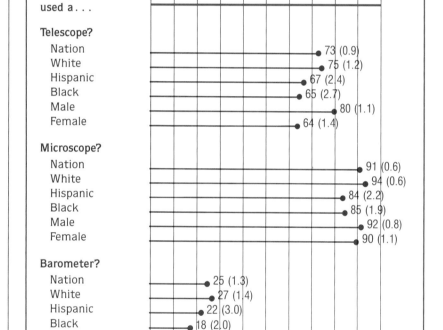

Have you ever used a...	Percent
Telescope?	
Nation	73 (0.9)
White	75 (1.2)
Hispanic	67 (2.4)
Black	65 (2.7)
Male	80 (1.1)
Female	64 (1.4)
Microscope?	
Nation	91 (0.6)
White	94 (0.6)
Hispanic	84 (2.2)
Black	85 (1.9)
Male	92 (0.8)
Female	90 (1.1)
Barometer?	
Nation	25 (1.3)
White	27 (1.4)
Hispanic	22 (3.0)
Black	18 (2.0)
Male	30 (1.5)
Female	20 (1.9)
Electricity Meter?	
Nation	21 (1.1)
White	22 (1.6)
Hispanic	22 (3.6)
Black	16 (1.4)
Male	31 (1.7)
Female	10 (1.1)

* Jackknifed standard errors are presented in parentheses.

THE NATION'S REPORT CARD

grade, use of telescopes was still far more common for boys than for girls in grade 7, as was the use of barometers and electricity meters.

It appears that the "experience gap" between White and minority students in some instances actually increased between grades 7 and 11. In addition, the gap between male and female students' use of scientific equip-

. . . use of telescopes was still far more common for boys than for girls in grade 7, as was the use of barometers and electricity meters.

Grade 11: Experience with Science Equipment for the Nation and Demographic Subgroups, 1986*

FIGURE 6.3B

Percent Responding "Yes"

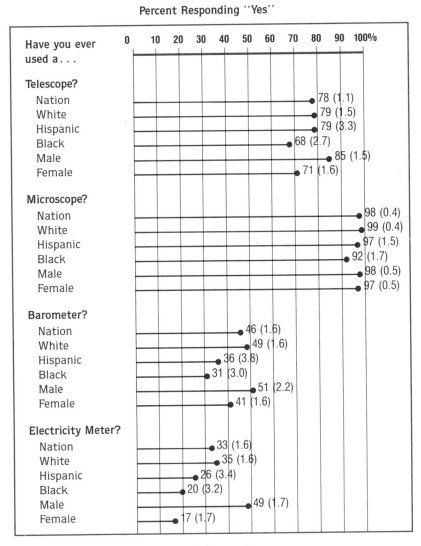

Have you ever used a. . .

Telescope?
Nation 78 (1.1)
White 79 (1.5)
Hispanic 79 (3.3)
Black 68 (2.7)
Male 85 (1.5)
Female 71 (1.6)

Microscope?
Nation 98 (0.4)
White 99 (0.4)
Hispanic 97 (1.5)
Black 92 (1.7)
Male 98 (0.5)
Female 97 (0.5)

Barometer?
Nation 46 (1.6)
White 49 (1.6)
Hispanic 36 (3.8)
Black 31 (3.0)
Male 51 (2.2)
Female 41 (1.6)

Electricity Meter?
Nation 33 (1.6)
White 35 (1.6)
Hispanic 26 (3.4)
Black 20 (3.2)
Male 49 (1.7)
Female 17 (1.7)

THE NATION'S REPORT CARD

* Jackknifed standard errors are presented in parentheses.

ment showed no signs of diminishing across the two upper grades. Overall, it appears that considerable disparities exist between the experience of White and minority students and that of male and female students in the use of scientific equipment.

Independent Science Activities

In addition to gathering information on students' experience using the tools of science, the 1986 assessment collected data on students' reported involvement in out-of-school science activities to provide a sense of the more informal paths of science learning that may be pursued for the sake of personal interest or motivation. FIGURE 6.4 provides responses to a series of questions on independent science experiences for the nation and performance quartiles.

Overall, a relatively small proportion of eleventh-grade students reported that they were engaged in any of the types of independent science activities mentioned. Only 39 percent of these high-school students read books or articles about the subject, and fewer engaged in science discussions with friends, trips to the museum, or science hobbies.

In all cases, students in the upper quartile of performance were more likely, often by a great margin, to report participating in out-of-school science activities. The differences between upper- and lower-quartile students were striking in all four activities—working on science hobbies, discussing science topics with friends, visiting the museum, and reading books or articles about science.

FIGURE 6.4

Grade 11: Independent Science Activities for the Nation and Selected Subgroups, 1986*

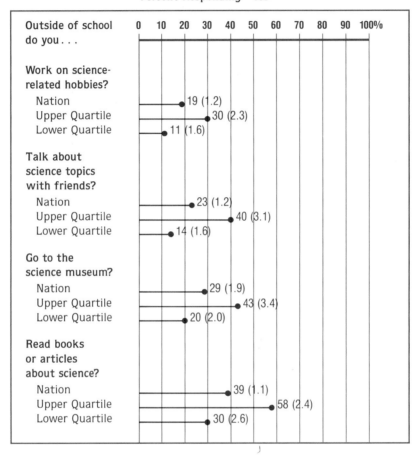

Percent Responding "Yes"

Outside of school do you . . .

Work on science-related hobbies?
- Nation — 19 (1.2)
- Upper Quartile — 30 (2.3)
- Lower Quartile — 11 (1.6)

Talk about science topics with friends?
- Nation — 23 (1.2)
- Upper Quartile — 40 (3.1)
- Lower Quartile — 14 (1.6)

Go to the science museum?
- Nation — 29 (1.9)
- Upper Quartile — 43 (3.4)
- Lower Quartile — 20 (2.0)

Read books or articles about science?
- Nation — 39 (1.1)
- Upper Quartile — 58 (2.4)
- Lower Quartile — 30 (2.6)

* Jackknifed standard errors are presented in parentheses.

THE NATION'S REPORT CARD **naep**

Applications of Science Knowledge

Students in grades 7 and 11 were asked to report on their efforts to apply science knowledge to practical situations in their lives. Although students were asked to report whether they had engaged in these activities "many times," "twice or more," "once or twice," or "never," only the percentages of students responding "many times" are reported here. Responses for the nation and selected subpopulations are presented in FIGURES 6.5A and 6.5B.

FIGURE 6.5A

Grade 7: Applications of Science Knowledge for the Nation and Selected Subgroups, 1986 *

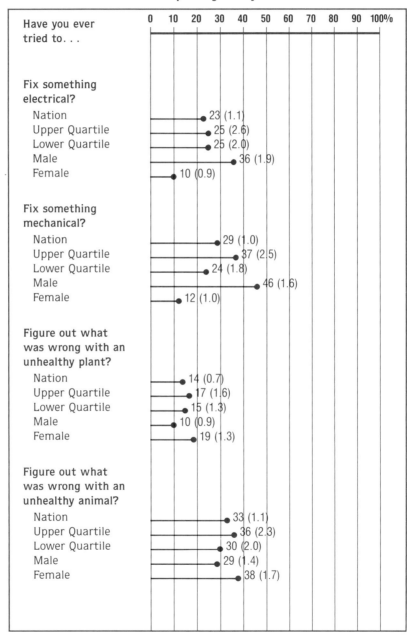

Percent Responding "Many Times"

Have you ever tried to. . .

Fix something electrical?

Nation	23 (1.1)
Upper Quartile	25 (2.6)
Lower Quartile	25 (2.0)
Male	36 (1.9)
Female	10 (0.9)

Fix something mechanical?

Nation	29 (1.0)
Upper Quartile	37 (2.5)
Lower Quartile	24 (1.8)
Male	46 (1.6)
Female	12 (1.0)

Figure out what was wrong with an unhealthy plant?

Nation	14 (0.7)
Upper Quartile	17 (1.6)
Lower Quartile	15 (1.3)
Male	10 (0.9)
Female	19 (1.3)

Figure out what was wrong with an unhealthy animal?

Nation	33 (1.1)
Upper Quartile	36 (2.3)
Lower Quartile	30 (2.0)
Male	29 (1.4)
Female	38 (1.7)

* Jackknifed standard errors are presented in parentheses.

THE NATION'S REPORT CARD

113

Grade 11: Applications of Science Knowledge for the Nation and Selected Subgroups, 1986*

FIGURE 6.5B

Percent Responding "Many Times"

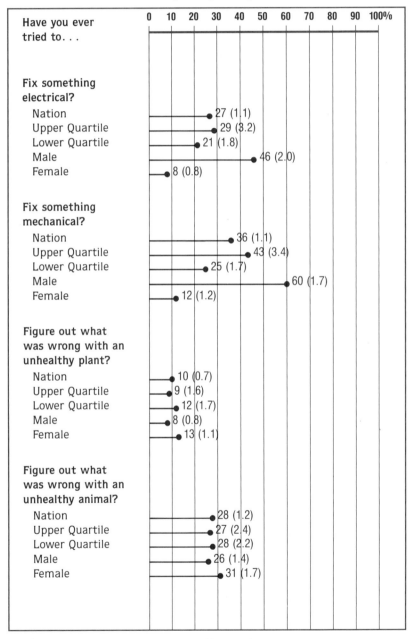

Have you ever tried to. . .

| | 0 | 10 | 20 | 30 | 40 | 50 | 60 | 70 | 80 | 90 | 100% |

Fix something electrical?
- Nation — 27 (1.1)
- Upper Quartile — 29 (3.2)
- Lower Quartile — 21 (1.8)
- Male — 46 (2.0)
- Female — 8 (0.8)

Fix something mechanical?
- Nation — 36 (1.1)
- Upper Quartile — 43 (3.4)
- Lower Quartile — 25 (1.7)
- Male — 60 (1.7)
- Female — 12 (1.2)

Figure out what was wrong with an unhealthy plant?
- Nation — 10 (0.7)
- Upper Quartile — 9 (1.6)
- Lower Quartile — 12 (1.7)
- Male — 8 (0.8)
- Female — 13 (1.1)

Figure out what was wrong with an unhealthy animal?
- Nation — 28 (1.2)
- Upper Quartile — 27 (2.4)
- Lower Quartile — 28 (2.2)
- Male — 26 (1.4)
- Female — 31 (1.7)

* Jackknifed standard errors are presented in parentheses.

THE NATION'S
REPORT
CARD

114

Students in the upper quartile in both grades were generally more likely than those in the lower quartile to report having applied their knowledge of science in the ways mentioned. It may be that students with higher science proficiency find more opportunities to apply their science knowledge in practical situations; alternatively, experience with everyday problems that require science knowledge may strengthen students' proficiency in the subject.

Some interesting variations were also evident by gender in students' reported experience in applying their science knowledge. In both grades, more males than females reported that they had attempted to fix something electrical or mechanical, while females were more likely to report having tried to diagnose an unhealthy plant or animal.

Trends in Participation in Conservation Efforts

Students at ages 13 and 17 were asked to report whether they had participated in recycling and conservation efforts as another indication of their out-of-school science activities. Although students were asked whether they had participated in litter clean-up or recycling efforts "often," "not often," "once or twice," or "never," only the extent to which students reported engaging in these activities "often" is presented here. TABLE 6.1 summarizes trends in 13- and 17-year-olds' reported participation in conservation-related activities from 1977 to 1986.

Ages 13 and 17: Trends in Participation in Conservation and Related Efforts, 1977-1986*		TABLE 6.1

	Percent Responding "Often"	
How many times have you. . .	1977	1986
Helped with a litter clean-up project?		
Age 13	13 (0.9)	13 (1.2)
Age 17	9 (0.9)	8 (1.2)
Separated trash for recycling?		
Age 13	13 (0.8)	23 (1.1)
Age 17	9 (0.6)	15 (1.3)

*Jackknifed standard errors are presented in parentheses.

Thirteen-year-olds were somewhat more likely than 17-year-olds to report frequent participation in conservation-related activities over the decade from 1977 to 1986. It is interesting to note that participation in litter clean-up efforts appears to have fallen for both seventh- and eleventh-graders since 1977, while involvement in recycling efforts has risen. Overall, it is perhaps surprising that so few students reported frequent participation in these activities, as youth organizations, clubs, and other extracurricular groups often sponsor recycling and conservation efforts in the community.

Summary

By the eleventh grade, a majority of students have gained exposure to various types of scientific equipment, such as microscopes, telescopes, and other apparatus, although from the earliest grades there are troubling disparities between the percentages of males and females who have these kinds of experiences, and between the percentages of White and minority students who do.

An analysis of students' endeavors to apply their science knowledge also revealed several interesting findings. Males reported more experience than did females in fixing electrical and mechanical problems; meanwhile, females reported more experience diagnosing unhealthy plants and animals. Few students reported having participated many times in conservation activities. These findings suggest the need to further expand out-of-school learning opportunities for all students, particularly for females and minorities historically thought to be at risk in science education.

... participation in litter clean-up efforts appears to have fallen for both seventh and eleventh graders since 1977 ...

CHAPTER 7
Home Support for Science Learning

Parental Involvement and Educational Support

P REVIOUS NAEP analyses have indicated that home support for and involvement in students' learning appears to be correlated with proficiency in various subject areas. To study this relationship in the context of science learning, the 1986 science assessment gathered information on parents' highest level of education; home assistance with science homework and projects; participation in science-related activities; the availability of reference materials in the home; and the amount of television viewed there.

Home Involvement in Science Learning

A majority of students in the third and seventh grades reported that they had someone at home with whom they discussed learning and from whom they received help on science projects.

Students in grades 3, 7, and 11 were asked to report on the extent to which someone from home participated in their science learning. Responses to this series of questions are provided in TABLE 7.1.

A majority of students in the third and seventh grades reported that they had someone at home with whom they discussed learning and from whom they received help on science projects. More than half of the students in grade 3 also reported reading science books with someone from home and receiving help with their science homework.

117

As may be expected, there is a sharp decline between grades 7 and 11 in the reported extent of home involvement in science learning. It is likely that the shift is tied to developmental issues—that is, students become more independent as they proceed through adolescence, reducing the opportuni-

| Grades 3, 7, and 11
Home Involvement in Science Learning for the
Nation and Performance Quartiles, 1986* | | | TABLE 7.1 |

Does anyone at home ever do the following things with you?	Percent Responding "Yes"		
	Grade 3	Grade 7	Grade 11
Talk about what you are learning.			
Nation	78 (1.5)	77 (1.1)	35 (1.2)
Upper Quartile	84 (2.2)	81 (2.2)	51 (2.9)
Lower Quartile	74 (2.2)	71 (2.4)	23 (1.8)
Help you with science homework.			
Nation	55 (1.5)	54 (1.3)	26 (1.8)
Upper Quartile	54 (2.5)	54 (2.4)	19 (2.1)
Lower Quartile	60 (2.3)	51 (2.6)	31 (3.8)
Help you work on a science project.			
Nation	64 (1.2)	59 (1.4)	31 (0.9)
Upper Quartile	68 (2.3)	61 (1.9)	31 (2.1)
Lower Quartile	55 (2.0)	56 (2.7)	27 (1.9)
Go to a science museum.			
Nation	37 (1.2)	33 (0.9)	23 (1.3)
Upper Quartile	41 (2.6)	46 (2.5)	35 (2.5)
Lower Quartile	38 (2.9)	22 (2.1)	15 (1.5)
Read books about science.			
Nation	59 (1.7)	35 (1.1)	19 (0.7)
Upper Quartile	57 (2.9)	31 (1.8)	22 (1.8)
Lower Quartile	67 (2.4)	42 (2.3)	18 (2.0)

*Jackknifed standard errors are presented in parentheses.

Data for the homework question at grade 11 represent only those students enrolled in a science class at the time of the assessment.

ties for home involvement in learning. For whatever reasons, only about one-third of the eleventh graders stated that they had someone at home with whom they discussed what they learned; and less than one-quarter reported home involvement in doing science homework and reading science books.

Upper-quartile students were more likely to report having discussions at home about what they had learned in school as well as receiving help with science projects and going on visits to science museums than were lower-quartile students. In contrast, lower-quartile students reported receiving help with doing science homework (except at grade 11) and reading science books more often than did upper-quartile students. The data suggest that students with the greatest need are receiving more support in these areas from someone at home.

Home Involvement in Science Learning by Parental Education

... the data suggest a "rich get richer" phenomenon, in which parents with higher levels of education are more involved in their children's science learning.

Parental education appears to play an important role in the extent of home support and involvement in science learning, as shown in TABLE 7.2. Students whose parents had pursued an education beyond the high-school level were more likely to report that someone at home participated in their science learning than were those whose parents had ended their education at or before high school. Thus, the data suggest a "rich get richer" phenomenon, in which parents with higher levels of education are more involved in their children's science learning by participating in projects, discussing ideas, and reading science books, and students with more of these experiences tend to have higher science proficiency scores.

Grades 3, 7, and 11: Home Involvement in Science Learning and Average Science Proficiency by Level of Parents' Education, 1986*	TABLE 7.2

Does anyone at home ever do the following things with you?	Parents' Highest Level of Education			
	Less than High School	Graduated High School	Courses Past High School	Graduated College
Talk about what you are learning.				
Percent "Yes"				
Grade 3	72 (4.6)	76 (3.2)	78 (4.4)	82 (2.3)
Grade 7	62 (3.9)	77 (1.9)	81 (2.8)	82 (1.6)
Grade 11	23 (3.4)	26 (1.4)	35 (2.6)	44 (2.5)
Help you work on a science project.				
Percent "Yes"				
Grade 3	56 (5.8)	60 (3.0)	70 (4.7)	68 (2.2)
Grade 7	57 (4.1)	58 (2.8)	57 (3.2)	63 (2.1)
Grade 11	23 (3.3)	28 (1.5)	31 (2.4)	35 (1.9)
Read books about science.				
Percent "Yes"				
Grade 3	53 (3.9)	59 (3.6)	58 (6.1)	59 (2.2)
Grade 7	32 (3.9)	34 (2.7)	30 (1.9)	36 (1.9)
Grade 11	18 (3.6)	16 (1.5)	18 (1.9)	23 (1.6)

*Jackknifed standard errors are presented in parentheses.

Access to Reading and Reference Materials in the Home

A positive relationship has been indicated in previous NAEP assessments between students' reading and writing proficiency and the availability of reading and reference materials in the home.[1] Does access to these materials

[1]Arthur N. Applebee, Judith A. Langer, and Ina V.S. Mullis, *Who Reads Best? Factors Related to Reading Achievement in Grades 3, 7, and 11* (Princeton, NJ: National Assessment of Educational Progress, Educational Testing Service, 1988).

Arthur N. Applebee, Judith A. Langer, and Ina V.S. Mullis, *The Writing Report Card: Writing Achievement in American Schools* (Princeton, NJ: National Assessment of Educational Progress, Educational Testing Service, 1986).

also appear to be related to science proficiency? To address this question, students were asked as part of the 1986 science assessment whether newspapers, books, magazines, a dictionary, and an encyclopedia were available to them at home. TABLE 7.3 summarizes the relationship between access to these reading and reference sources and science proficiency for students in grades 3, 7, and 11.

Grades 3, 7, and 11: Average Science Proficiency by Number of Reading and Reference Materials in the Home, 1986*			TABLE 7.3

| Reading and Reference Materials in the Home** | Average Science Proficiency | | |
	Grade 3	Grade 7	Grade 11
0-3	199 (1.0)	227 (0.8)	264 (1.2)
4	217 (1.0)	247 (0.8)	286 (1.2)
5	227 (1.0)	260 (0.7)	299 (1.0)

*Jackknifed standard errors are presented in parentheses.

**Students were asked about five types of reading and reference materials—a dictionary, an encyclopedia, books, newspapers, and magazines.

At all three grades, students with access to more reading and reference materials at home had higher science achievement . . .

At all three grades, students with access to more reading and reference materials at home had higher science achievement than did students who had access to fewer materials. As questions of cause and effect cannot be addressed by the data, one cannot say whether the availability of newspapers, dictionaries, and other educational materials improves students' science proficiency, or whether more proficient students simply have more of these materials in their homes. Regardless of the direction of the relationship, however, it may be argued that all students should have access to varied reading and reference materials at home for educational use.

Television Viewing

As with previous NAEP assessments in other subject areas, the 1986 science assessment asked students to report the amount of television that they watched each day. The relationship between television viewing and science proficiency is summarized in TABLE 7.4.

The relationship between hours of daily television viewing and science proficiency appears to be generally negative at all three grades, despite some variations in this pattern. At grades 3 and 7, there was little difference in the

	Average Science Proficiency		
Hours of Daily Television Viewing	**Grade 3**	**Grade 7**	**Grade 11**
0-2	217 (1.0)	256 (1.7)	303 (1.2)
3-5	222 (1.0)	253 (0.7)	284 (0.8)
6 or more	200 (0.9)	232 (0.9)	265 (1.7)

*Jackknifed standard errors are presented in parentheses.

Grades 3, 7, and 11: Average Science Proficiency by Amount of Daily Television Viewing, 1986*

TABLE 7.4

science proficiency of those who reported zero to two hours and those who reported three to five hours of daily television viewing. Across the grades, however, students who reported watching six or more hours of television each day registered science proficiency considerably below that of their peers who reported lesser amounts of television viewing.

... students who reported watching six or more hours of television each day registered science proficiency considerably below that of their peers who reported lesser amounts of television viewing.

Summary

Given that learning is a multifaceted process and that influences upon students' interest and performance may derive from many sources, it is useful to consider not only the in-school education to which students have been exposed, but also the education that arises from the home environment.

Data from the 1986 NAEP science assessment indicate that students with higher science proficiency were more likely to report home involvement in science projects and activities, access to more types of reading and reference materials at home, and lesser amounts of television viewing.

CHAPTER 8
How Students Perceive Science

Student Views on the Utility and Value of Science Learning

General Attitudes Toward Science

STUDENTS IN grades 3, 7, and 11 were asked to convey their attitudes toward science learning. Did they enjoy science or find it boring? Did they perceive that science classes were relevant to everyday experiences? Did they believe that science knowledge would be part of their life's work?

Seventh- and eleventh-grade students' responses to these and related questions were used to construct a background indicator that grouped students' attitudes toward science into three levels—high (positive), medium (neutral), or low (negative). FIGURE 8.1 presents students' average science proficiency by their general attitudes toward science, as reflected in the background indicator.

A positive relationship appears to exist between attitudes toward science and proficiency in the subject, particularly among eleventh-grade students. Students who enjoy science, believe that knowledge of the subject has practical applications, and perceive that science will be a part of their future work are likely to have higher proficiency than students with less positive attitudes toward the subject. Although questions of cause and effect cannot

Students who enjoy science, believe that knowledge of the subject has practical applications, and perceive that science will be a part of their future work are likely to have higher proficiency ...

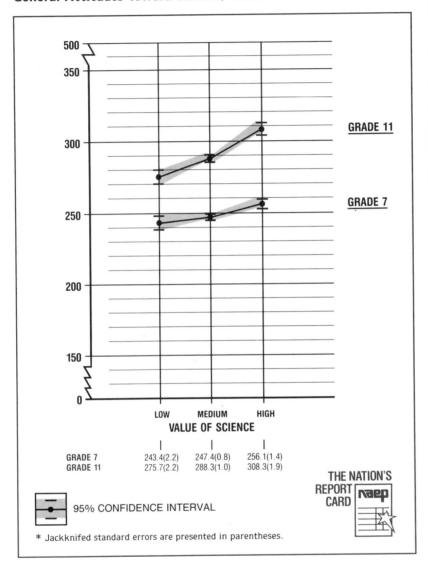

	LOW	MEDIUM	HIGH
GRADE 7	243.4(2.2)	247.4(0.8)	256.1(1.4)
GRADE 11	275.7(2.2)	288.3(1.0)	308.3(1.9)

THE NATION'S
REPORT
CARD

95% CONFIDENCE INTERVAL

* Jackknifed standard errors are presented in parentheses.

be answered by the data—that is, one cannot know if positive attitudes render higher proficiency, or vice versa—it is plausible that the two interact in a complementary manner.

Given research evidence that females are less likely than males to enroll in high-school science classes or enter careers in science and engineering, NAEP was interested in exploring gender differences in attitudes toward science.[1] FIGURE 8.2 presents males' and females' responses to three attitudinal questions, compared with responses for the nation as a whole.

In both grades 7 and 11, males tend to have more positive attitudes toward science than do females. Gender differences were relatively small in response to the item asking whether students believed that science would help them to earn a living; however, they were slightly larger in response to the items concerning the importance of science in life and the uses of science knowledge as an adult. There appears to be little change in the magnitude of these gender differences between grades 7 and 11.

[1]Michael F. Crowley, *Women and Minorities in Science and Engineering* (Washington, DC: National Science Foundation, Division of Science Resources Studies, 1986).

Task Force on Women, Minorities, and the Handicapped in Science and Technology, *Changing America: The New Face of Science and Engineering* (Washington, DC, 1988).

Grades 7 and 11: Perceptions of the Personal Relevance of Science Knowledge for the Nation and Demographic Subgroups, 1986*

FIGURE 8.2

Percent Responding "Strongly Agree" or "Agree"

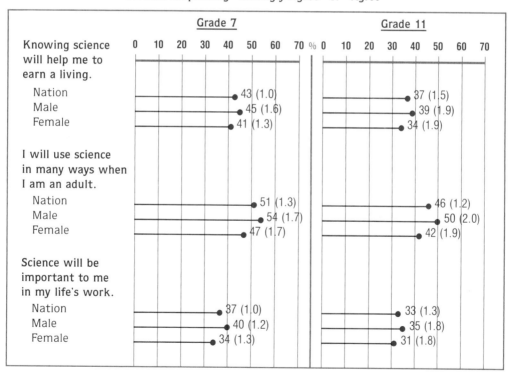

* Jackknifed standard errors are presented in parentheses.

What is perhaps more salient in these responses than differences between the attitudes of males and females is the fact that so few students overall reportedly believe that science knowledge will be useful or relevant in their lives. Less than half of the seventh graders—and even fewer eleventh graders—perceived that science would help them to earn a living, be important to them in life, or be used in many ways during adulthood.

Positive attitudes toward science (or any other subject area) are seen by most educators to be an important outcome of schooling.[2] To assess changes in students' attitudes toward science across the school years, third-grade students were asked to report their views on science learning. Their responses are summarized in TABLE 8.1.

Grade 3: Attitudes Toward Science, 1986*	TABLE 8.1

	Percent Responding "Yes"
When you have science in school, do you like it?	67 (1.8)
When you have science in school, does it make you feel interested?	78 (1.5)
Are things you learn in science useful to you when you are not in school?	67 (1.5)
Do you think that knowing a lot about science will help when you grow up?	71 (1.2)

*Jackknifed standard errors are presented in parentheses.

Although most third-grade students appeared to value science—reporting that what they learned in the subject was useful, enjoyable, and interesting—between one-third and one-quarter of the young students did not share these views. A comparison of reported attitudes at grade 3 with those at grades 7 and 11 supports the finding from NAEP's most recent mathematics report that positive attitudes decline as students progress through school.[3]

[2]Richard J. Murnane and Senta A. Raizen, eds., *Improving Indicators of the Quality of Science and Mathematics Education in Grades K-12* (Washington, DC: National Academy Press, 1988).

[3]John A. Dossey, Ina V.S. Mullis, Mary M. Lindquist, and Donald L. Chambers, *The Mathematics Report Card: Are We Measuring Up? Trends and Achievement Based on the 1986 National Assessment* (Princeton, NJ: National Assessment of Educational Progress, Educational Testing Service, 1988).

Trends in Attitudes Toward Science

Several attitudinal items were held constant from previous assessments to permit analysis of trends in students' attitudes toward science learning. TABLE 8.2 presents trends in 13- and 17-year-old students' views of the importance and utility of science knowledge.

Ages 13 and 17: Trends in Attitudes Toward Science, 1977-1986*				TABLE 8.2

	Percent Responding "Strongly Agree" or "Agree"			
	Age 13		Age 17	
	1977	1986	1977	1986
Much of what you learn in science classes is useful in everyday life.	57 (1.2)	54 (1.9)	53 (1.0)	49 (1.6)
Much of what you learn in science classes will be useful in the future.	74 (1.4)	73 (1.5)	65 (1.1)	65 (1.3)
Science should be required in school.	70 (1.4)	70 (1.3)	62 (1.0)	70 (1.6)

*Jackknifed standard errors are presented in parentheses.

Attitudes toward the utility of science learning appear to have changed little across time. In 1986, only about one-half of the 13- and 17-year-olds perceived that science learning was useful in everyday life, and about two-thirds of the 17-year-olds (65 percent) felt that what they learned in science classes would be useful in the future. Slightly more of these high-school students (70 percent) believed that science should be required in school. Overall, trends in students' attitudes toward science reveal few uniform patterns across the age groups and across time, and do little to illuminate recent trends toward improved student performance in the subject.

Perceived Applications of Science

Seventh- and eleventh-grade students were asked whether they believed that science could be applied to help remedy particular global problems—

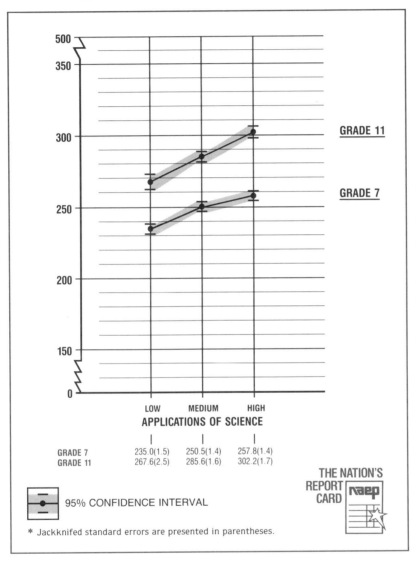

including such human problems as world starvation, disease, overpopulation, and birth defects and such environmental problems as depletion of natural resources, air and water pollution, and destruction of the ozone layer. Responses to these questions were combined in a background indicator which grouped students' perceptions of the applications of science into three levels—high (positive), medium (neutral), and low (negative). FIGURE 8.3

provides a view of the relationship between students' science proficiency and their perceived applications of science.

Perhaps a greater classroom emphasis on the applications of science would build students' appreciation of the utility and relevance of scientific work.

Students who perceived numerous applications of scientific knowledge to world problems tended to have higher science proficiency than those who did not, although the direction of this relationship is unknown. Perhaps a greater classroom emphasis on the applications of science would build students' appreciation of the utility and relevance of scientific work.

Trends in Perceived Applications of Science

Several questions on the applications of science were maintained from previous assessments to provide for an analysis of attitudinal trends, as shown in TABLE 8.3. In both 1977 and 1986, 17-year-olds were more likely than 13-year-olds to perceive that scientific knowledge could be applied to help resolve national and global problems of the types listed. Students were more

Ages 13 and 17: Trends in Perceived Applications of Science, 1977-1986*

TABLE 8.3

How much do you think that the application of science can help. . .	Age	Percent Responding "Very Much"	
		1977	1986
Prevent world starvation?	13	32 (1.5)	25 (1.7)
	17	50 (1.2)	33 (1.3)
Save us from an energy shortage?	13	54 (1.8)	60 (2.4)
	17	70 (1.0)	71 (1.3)
Find cures for diseases?	13	70 (1.5)	69 (1.6)
	17	85 (0.8)	83 (1.1)
Control weather?	13	15 (0.9)	16 (1.3)
	17	16 (0.8)	19 (0.8)
Prevent birth defects?	13	23 (1.2)	34 (1.8)
	17	44 (1.2)	51 (1.3)
Save our natural resources?	13	46 (1.1)	50 (1.5)
	17	48 (1.2)	55 (1.4)
Reduce air and water pollution?	13	44 (1.3)	49 (1.9)
	17	54 (1.2)	57 (1.4)

*Jackknifed standard errors are presented in parentheses.

likely in 1986 than in 1977 to agree that the applications of science could help to preserve natural resources, reduce air and water pollution, and prevent birth defects. The largest changes across time were the decreases in the percentages of 13- and particularly 17-year-olds who believed that science applications could help to resolve the problem of world starvation. Although the data cannot shed light on the reasons for this change, perhaps students are becoming more cognizant that multiple conditions—political, economic, and social, as well as agricultural—may contribute to world starvation, and that many of these conditions confound scientific solutions.

Attitudes Toward Professional Ethics in Science

In addition to asking students to report on their enjoyment of science and their views on the utility and relevance of scientific work, the 1986 assessment asked students to convey their attitudes toward science as a profession and, in particular, their views on questions of ethics. Responses for students in grades 7 and 11 are provided in TABLE 8.4.

Grades 7 and 11: Attitudes Toward Professional Ethics in Science, 1986*		TABLE 8.4

How often do you think scientists should be allowed to. . .	Percent Responding "Never"	
	Grade 7	Grade 11
Experiment on people without their approval?	68 (1.2)	81 (1.0)
Create diseases for warfare?	61 (1.5)	73 (1.2)
Work on secret projects?	15 (0.8)	14 (0.9)

*Jackknifed standard errors are presented in parentheses.

Eleventh graders were more likely than seventh graders to respond negatively when asked whether scientists should experiment on people without approval or create new diseases for warfare. Students in both grades were equally likely to believe that scientists should never work on secret projects. Overall, the percentage of students in either seventh or eleventh grade that denounced these activities may be lower than expected.

Trends in Attitudes Toward Professional Ethics in Science

The NAEP data reveal several interesting changes across time in students' attitudes toward ethical questions in the science profession. TABLE 8.5 presents attitudinal trends from 1977 to 1986 in 13- and 17-year-olds' responses to the three ethical questions previously described.

Ages 13 and 17: Trends in Attitudes Toward Professional Ethics in Science, 1977-1986*

TABLE 8.5

How often do you think scientists should be allowed to. . .	Percent Responding "Never"	
	1977	1986
Experiment on people without their approval?		
Age 13	76 (1.2)	82 (1.4)
Age 17	81 (1.1)	85 (1.0)
Create new diseases for warfare?		
Age 13	70 (1.4)	64 (1.7)
Age 17	81 (1.1)	77 (1.2)
Work on secret projects?		
Age 13	8 (0.6)	11 (0.7)
Age 17	9 (0.5)	15 (1.2)

*Jackknifed standard errors are presented in parentheses.

Across time, there appears to have been a significant increase in the proportion of students in each age group who believe that scientists should never experiment on people without approval, or work on secret projects. Conversely, fewer students in 1986 believed that scientists should never be engaged in the production of diseases for use in warfare.

Summary

Most students in the third, seventh, and eleventh grades appear to be unenthusiastic about the value and personal relevance of their science learning, and their attitudes seem to decline as they progress through school. These findings parallel those of the 1986 mathematics assessment, which found that students' appreciation of mathematics learning also deteriorated across the grades.[4] In addition, trend data indicate that slightly fewer students in 1986 than in previous assessment years believed that science knowledge was either useful in their everyday lives or would be in the future. There were few changes in the percentages of students who believed that science should be a required subject in schools.

Asked whether science knowledge could help to resolve certain national and global problems, either human or environmental, more students in 1986 than a decade ago believed that science could be used to prevent birth defects, save natural resources, and reduce air and water pollution. Fewer students believed that science could prevent world starvation or find cures for diseases.

As a whole, students in the eleventh grade appeared to have more ethical views on the conduct of scientific work than did those in the seventh grade. That is, students in the upper grade were more likely to state that scientists should never experiment on people without approval, nor create diseases for warfare. However, students in both grades were equally likely to agree that scientists should never work on secret projects.

There appear to be few consistent relationships between these trends in reported attitudes and students' observed science proficiency, raising new questions about what factors may have contributed to recent gains in performance seen in the 1986 NAEP science assessment. Although the responses to attitudinal questions reveal few consistent themes, the findings do provide some cause for hope. Despite lukewarm opinions about the relevance of science instruction to their current and future lives, many students believe that scientific knowledge is useful and can be applied to resolve pressing national and global problems. As part of the effort to strengthen our students' proficiency in science, educators and parents should encourage more constructive views of the relevance and utility of scientific knowledge.

Most students in the third, seventh, and eleventh grades appear to be unenthusiastic about the value and personal relevance of their science learning . . .

. . . more students in 1986 than a decade ago believed that science could be used to prevent birth defects, save natural resources, and reduce air and water pollution.

. . . educators and parents should encourage more constructive views of the relevance and utility of scientific knowledge.

---

[4]John A. Dossey, Ina V.S. Mullis, Mary M. Lindquist, and Donald L. Chambers, *The Mathematics Report Card: Are We Measuring Up? Trends and Achievement Based on the 1986 National Assessment* (Princeton, NJ: National Assessment of Educational Progress, Educational Testing Service, 1988).

PROCEDURAL APPENDIX

T HE NATION'S Report Card, the National Assessment of Educational Progress (NAEP), is an ongoing, congressionally-mandated project established to conduct national surveys of the educational performance of young Americans. Its primary goal is to determine and report the status of and trends over time in educational achievement. NAEP was created in 1969 to obtain comprehensive and dependable national educational achievement data in a uniform, scientific manner. Today, NAEP remains the only regularly-conducted national survey of educational achievement at the elementary-, middle-, and high-school levels.

Since 1969, NAEP has assessed 9-, 13-, and 17-year-olds attending public and private schools. In 1983, NAEP began sampling students by grade as well as by age. Because the 1985-86 assessment was the first to include grade-level samples for science, the trend results presented in this report are based on comparable samples of students at ages 9, 13, and 17. Some 1986 results are also presented for students in the third, seventh, and eleventh grades.

The subject areas assessed by NAEP have included reading, writing, mathematics, science, and social studies, as well as citizenship, computer understanding, literature, art, music, and career development. Assessments were conducted annually through 1980 and have been conducted biennially since then. Recent assessments have included reading, writing, mathematics, science, computer competence, literacy, literature, and U.S. history. In the 1987-88 school year, NAEP assessed reading, writing, civics, U.S. history, and geography. All subjects except career development and computer understanding and computer competence have been reassessed to determine trends in achievement over time. To date, NAEP has surveyed approximately 1,300,000 American students. In addition, NAEP periodically samples young adults.

From its inception, NAEP has developed assessments through a consensus process. Educators, scholars, and citizens representative of many diverse constituencies and points of view design objectives for each subject-area assessment, proposing general goals they feel students should achieve in the course of their education. After careful reviews, the objectives are given to item writers, who develop assessment questions appropriate to the objectives.

All questions undergo extensive reviews by subject-matter and measurement specialists, as well as careful scrutiny to eliminate any potential bias or lack of sensitivity to particular groups. They are then field-tested, revised, and administered to a stratified, multistage probability sample. The young people sampled are selected so that their results may be generalized to the entire national population. Once the data have been collected, scored, and analyzed, NAEP publishes and disseminates the results. Its purpose is to provide information that will help educators, legislators, and others to monitor and improve education in the United States.

To enhance the utility of NAEP achievement results and provide the opportunity to examine policy issues, NAEP has recently begun to collect information about numerous background issues. Students, teachers, and school officials answer a variety of questions about demographics, education-related activities and experiences, attitudes, curriculum, and resources.

NAEP is supported by the U.S. Department of Education, Office for Educational Research and Improvement, National Center for Education Statistics. In 1983, Educational Testing Service assumed responsibility for the administration of the project, which had previously been administered by the Education Commission of the States. NAEP is governed by an independent, legislatively-defined board.

General Background of NAEP's Science Assessments

NAEP has assessed the science achievement of in-school 9-, 13-, and 17-year-olds five times: in the 1969-70 school year, in 1972-73, in 1976-77, in 1981-82,[1] and in 1985-86. In 1986, NAEP also measured the achievement of third-, seventh-, and eleventh-grade students.

With an exception in 1969-70, each trend assessment of the three age groups was conducted as follows: 13-year-olds were assessed in the fall (October-December), 9-year-olds in the winter (January-February), and 17-year-olds in the spring (March-May). For the 1969-70 assessment, 17-year-olds were assessed in the spring of the preceding academic year (1968-69). Birth-date ranges for each age group in the four trend assessments follow:

Assessment	Age 9	Age 13	Age 17
1969-70	1960	1956	10/51-9/52
1972-73	1963	1959	10/55-9/56
1976-77	1967	1963	10/59-9/60
1981-82	1972	1968	10/64-9/65
1985-86	1976	1972	10/68-9/69

For the grade-level assessment in 1986, all students were assessed in the spring (February-March). The target populations consisted of 9-, 13-, and 17-year-olds enrolled in public and private elementary and secondary schools and other students in the modal grades for those ages. So that the modal grades for the three age groups would be third, seventh, and eleventh grades, the age definitions of 9- and 13-year-olds were different from those used for the trend assessments. The birth-date range for age-eligible 9-year-olds was 10/76—9/77 and for 13-year-olds, 10/72—9/73.

Content of the Science Assessments

Each science assessment contained a range of open-ended and multiple-choice questions measuring performance on sets of objectives developed by nationally-representative panels of science specialists, educators, and concerned citizens.[2] The objectives for each successive assessment were based on the framework used for the previous assessment with some revisions that reflected content changes and trends in school science.

In each assessment, NAEP asked students to answer questions across a range of content areas (e.g., Life Sciences, Physics, Chemistry, Earth and Space Sciences, and history of science); context areas (e.g., scientific, personal, societal, and technological); and cognitive areas (e.g., knowledge, use, and integration). Although changes were made from assessment to assessment, a small set of exercises was kept constant in order to anchor the results across time.

Sampling and the Trend Assessments

All NAEP assessments are based on a deeply stratified three-stage sampling design. The first stage entails defining primary sampling units (PSUs)—typically counties, but sometimes

[1]The 1982 assessment was conducted by the University of Minnesota under a grant from the National Science Foundation. See Stacey J. Hueftle, Steven J. Rakow, and Wayne W. Welch, *Images of Science: A Summary of Results from the 1981-82 National Assessment of Science* (Minneapolis, MN: Science Assessment and Research Project, University of Minnesota, 1983).

[2]National Assessment of Educational Progress, *Science Objectives: 1985-86 Assessment* (Princeton, NJ: Educational Testing Service, 1987).

aggregates of small counties; classifying the PSUs into strata defined by region and community type; and randomly selecting PSUs. For each age level, the second stage entails enumerating, stratifying, and randomly selecting schools, both public and private, within each PSU selected at the first stage. The third stage involves randomly selecting students within a school for participation in NAEP. Some students sampled (less than 5 percent) are excluded because of limited English proficiency or severe handicap. In 1984, NAEP also began collecting descriptive information about these excluded students.

Student Sample Sizes for Science Trend Scaling					TABLE A.1
	1970	**1973**	**1977**	**1982**	**1986**
Age 9	19,468	20,862	17,345	1,960	6,932
Age 13	21,696	23,507	25,653	7,873	6,200
Age 17 (in-school)	22,913	25,865	31,436	7,974	3,868

School Cooperation and Student Response Rates			TABLE A.2
	Age	**Percent Schools Participating**	**Percent Student Completion**
1970*	9	—	88.0
	13	—	85.6
	17	—	74.5
1973*	9	93.9	91.0
	13	93.8	84.6
	17	92.4	73.6
1977*	9	91.5	88.6
	13	91.3	86.2
	17	89.5	73.1
1982*	9	88.3	90.5
	13	89.2	85.5
	17	86.5	74.2
1986**	9	88.7	92.9
	13	88.1	89.2
	17	82.7	78.9

*1970, 1973, 1977, and 1982 figures obtained from corresponding *Public Use Data Tape User Guides.* School participation data is unavailable for 1970.
**1986 figures obtained from Westat, Inc., *National Assessment of Educational Progress—17th Year, Sampling and Weighting Procedures.*

For the portion of the assessment designed to measure trends, students were administered previously-assessed science questions according to the procedures used in prior assessments. Seventy-nine questions were given at age 9, 112 at age 13, and 111 at age 17, with each of the booklets accompanied by a paced audio recording of the questions as was done in the first 4 assessments. Because the 1986 design involved measuring trends in different subject areas at different age levels, 9-, 13-, and 17-year-olds were administered one of three booklets containing science trend items.

Sample sizes for the trend results in this report and cooperation rates for the 1970, 1973, 1977, 1982, and 1986 assessments are presented in TABLES A.1 and A.2.

The 1986 Assessment

The 1986 assessment design underlying the grade-level results was based on a variant of matrix sampling called Balanced Incomplete Block (BIB) spiralling. As part of this design, for each subject area assessed (reading, mathematics, and computer competence, as well as science) and for each grade level, the entire 1986 assessment battery was divided into blocks of approximately 15 minutes each, and each student was administered a booklet containing three blocks of content-area materials as well as a six-minute block of background questions common to all students. Seven blocks of science questions were assessed at grade 3, nine blocks at grade 7, and eleven blocks at grade 11.

As part of the partial BIB design, each pair of blocks within a subject area appeared in at least one assessment booklet. In addition, some blocks were paired across subject areas. At grade 3, 52 different booklets were prepared. Thirty-two of them contained one or more science blocks, with each of the seven blocks appearing in six to eight booklets. Sixty-eight booklets were assessed at grade 7, 37 of which contained science blocks; each science block appeared in six to nine different booklets. Science items were included in 44 of the 96 booklets administered to students at grade 11, with each block appearing seven to nine times.

The spiralling part of the method cycles the booklets for administration so that typically only a few students in any assessment session receive the same booklet. Across all the booklets, the grade-level results contained in this report were based on 11,046 students at grade 3; 12,142 students at grade 7; and 11,744 students at grade 11.

Data Collection and Scoring

NAEP's 1985-86 science assessment was conducted by a professional data collection staff managed by Westat, Inc. Quality control was provided through site visits by NAEP and Westat staff members.

After trained readers scored the open-ended questions, the booklets were scanned and the information transferred to the NAEP data base. These activities were conducted with particular care given to quality control procedures.

Teacher Questionnaire

In 1986, NAEP began collecting data on teacher attributes, as reported by teachers of students participating in the NAEP assessments. The purpose of this effort was to determine the proportion of students' teachers who had certain attributes; since it is not a random sample, however, the results cannot be generalized to describe teachers nationwide.

To select the sample of teachers to whom the questionnaire would be administered, a subsample of students was chosen from the total population of students participating in each assessment session within each school. The school coordinator was then asked to identify the teacher of a particular subject for each student selected, and these teachers were asked to complete the questionnaire. As teachers at grade 3/age 9 tend to teach all or most subjects, teachers of specific subjects were not distinguished at this grade level. At grade 7/age 13, teachers were selected for English/language arts, mathematics, or science, and at grade 11/age 17, for English/language arts, mathematics, science, or U.S. history. This report contains responses only for teachers of science at grades 7 and 11, and for all teachers at grade 3. Teachers who were identified by more than one student within a school were asked to complete just one questionnaire, to avoid duplications.

Sample sizes for science teachers who completed the questionnaire are presented below (TABLE A.3).

The teacher questionnaire asked those surveyed to provide general information on their demographic characteristics, type of teaching certification, educational background, and years of teaching experience at various grade levels. In addition, it requested information specific to science instruction, including the types of classroom activities undertaken, the amount of homework assigned each week, and the extent of laboratory or other instructional resources. Future analyses may permit examination of relationships between students' science proficiency and teacher characteristics.

Analysis and IRT Scaling

After NAEP data were scored, they were weighted in accordance with the population structure and adjusted for nonresponse. Analyses included computing the percentage of students giving various responses and using Item Response Theory (IRT) technology to estimate levels of science achievement for the nation and for various subpopulations.

Using IRT technology, the performance of a sample of students in a learning area or subarea can be summarized on a single scale even if different students have been administered different exercises. The underlying principle is that when a number of items require similar skills, the regularities observed across patterns of responses can often be used to characterize both respondents and tasks in terms of a relatively small number of variables. When aggregated through appropriate mathematical formulas, these variables capture the dominant features of the data. Using the scale, it becomes possible to talk about distributions of proficiency in a population or subpopulation, and to estimate the relationships between proficiency and background variables.

IRT defines the probability of answering a given item correctly as a mathematical function of proficiency level or skill and certain characteristics of the item. (Specifically, NAEP uses a three-parameter logistic model.) NAEP's statistical estimates of national and subgroup proficiency are computed as expected values of the figures that would have been obtained had individual proficiencies been observed, given the data that were in fact observed—the responses to the science exercises and to background items. (For theoretical justification of the procedures employed and computational details, see *Implementing the New Design: The NAEP 1983-84 Technical Report*.)

The development of scales was carried out separately for the 1985-86 grade/age data and the trend data. The details of the scaling processes used appear below.

Scaling of the 1986 Grade/Age Science Data

The analysis of the grade-level results of the 1986 science assessment (BIB-spiral design) was

Science Teacher Sample Sizes for Teacher Questionnaire, 1986	TABLE A.3

Grade Level	Number of Respondents
Grade 3 (all teachers)	774
Grade 7 (science teachers only)	325
Grade 11 (science teachers only)	289

carried out based on 396 items in six content-area subscales. Five subscales were developed at grades 7 and 11—Nature of Science, Life Sciences, Chemistry, Physics, and Earth and Space Sciences. At grade 3, the Nature of Science and Life Sciences subscales were used, but the areas of Physics and Chemistry were combined into a single Physical Sciences subscale, and there were an insufficient number of items given in the area of Earth and Space Sciences to develop a scale.

The overall composite was developed as a weighted average of subscale results. (Although this report is based on results for the grade-level samples from the 1986 assessment, the age-level samples were also scaled.) Each of the subscales was defined to correspond to a particular content area of science as defined by the NAEP publication *Science Objectives, 1985-86 Assessment*.[3] The subscales were created to allow the detection of potential differences in performance patterns between content areas. The identification of the subscales, along with the number of items appearing in each subscale at each grade/age, is shown in TABLE A.4.

The subscales were constructed along the same lines as the NAEP undimensional scales (such as Reading) with the major differences being that item parameters were estimated separately within each subscale and that, rather than estimating a single, univariate measure of proficiency, a multivariate vector of proficiencies, one for each subscale, was estimated for each student.

Like all IRT scales, the science subscales have a linear indeterminacy that may be resolved by an arbitrary choice of the origin and unit-size in each given subscale. The linear indeterminacies of the science subscales were resolved in three steps. In the first step, intermediate transformations of each of the subscales were applied so that the age-group differences across the various subscales would be approximately equal to each other. For the two subscales that spanned all three grades/ages, the intermediate transformation was accomplished by matching the subscale means at ages 9 and 17 to the corresponding averages of the age-group means across the two subscales. Note that this method permits means to vary for the age 13 samples. For Chemistry,

---

[3]One of the content areas defined by the *Science Objectives* book (History of Science) had an insufficient number of items to support the creation of a subscale at any age level.

Identification of Science Subscales

TABLE A.4

Subscale	Number of Items			
	Total	Grade 3/ Age 9	Grade 7/ Age 13	Grade 11/ Age 17
Life Science	116	39	44	59
Chemistry	55	—	23	44
Physics	62	—	30	44
Physical Science (Physics and Chemistry combined)	44	44	—	—
Earth and Space Science	52	—	42	39
Nature of Science	67	17	33	36

Physics, and Earth and Space Sciences, subscales that appeared in only the higher two age-groups, the age 17 means were matched to the average of the age 17 means across the three-age-spanning subscales, but the age 13 mean was matched to the average transformed age 13 mean obtained in the two science subscales that spanned all three ages. For the Physical Sciences subscale, which appeared only at age 9, the mean was set to the average of the age 9 subscale means (again over the three-age-spanning subscales), and the standard deviation was set to the average of the age 9 standard deviations. This method of scale determination constrains the age 9 means to be equal across subscales and the age 17 means to be equal across subscales, but the age 13 means can be expected to vary slightly.

The next step in resolving the linear indeterminacies of the subscales was the creation of an intermediate overall science composite. This intermediate composite was defined separately for each grade/age as a weighted average of the estimated student proficiencies (plausible values) for the subscales appearing in that grade/age (after the intermediate transformations), with weights that reflect the number of items in that subscale on the assessment for that grade/age. (The number of items per subscale constitutes the Science Learning Area Committee's implicit weighting of that subscale's relative importance.) The definition of the intermediate composite in each grade/age is given in TABLE A.5.

The final step in the creation of the science subscales and the composite scale was to linearly transform the intermediate composite scale so that the final composite would have a weighted mean of 250.5 and a weighted standard deviation of 50 across all students in the three ages. The same linear transformation that created the final composite was then applied to each of the intermediate science subscales.

It is necessary to caution that, although the science composite is expressed in apparently the same units as the 1984 reading proficiency scale, in that both scales have similar means and standard deviations, it is not appropriate to compare scores on one scale with scores on the other. The transformation chosen to resolve the linear indeterminacies in the science composite is a convenient transformation, but it is only one of a con-

Defining Weights for Composite Science Scale*			TABLE A.5
Subscale	**Grade 3/ Age 9**	**Grade 7/ Age 13**	**Grade 11/ Age 17**
Life Science	44	27	26
Chemistry	33	17	21
Physics	—	17	21
Earth and Space Science	0	22	16
Nature of Science	23	17	16
	100	100	100

*See National Assessment of Educational Progress. *Science Objectives: 1985-86 Assessment*. Princeton, NJ: Educational Testing Service, 1987 (p. 11).

At grade 3/Age 9, the Physics and Chemistry subscales were merged to form a single Physical Science Subscale.

ceptually infinite number of such transformations that could have been chosen, any one of which would have provided equivalent information about the relative standings of population subgroups in terms of their abilities in science. Because there was no link, real or implied, between science and reading in the construction of the science composite and the science subscales, the comparison of the mean proficiencies of a subgroup on science with the mean proficiencies of that subgroup on reading is not warranted and is devoid of meaning.

Scaling of the Science Trend Data

As explained previously, the measurement of trends in science achievement over time was based on a somewhat different sample from that used for the 1986 grade-level results. In contrast to the BIB-spiral administration, where students read items silently to themselves in timed blocks, the method of administration in previous NAEP science assessments used tape recordings to read items and pace students through the session. Furthermore, the range of birth dates that defined 9- and 13-year-old students was different in the BIB-spiral administration than in previous assessments. Bridge samples of pace-administered science items were included in the 1985-86 assessment in order to enable comparisons with previous NAEP assessments. To adjust for the changes in age definition in the case of 9- and 13-year-old students, two separate bridge samples of pace-administered items were included in the assessment, one using the old age definitions and one the definitions used in the BIB-spiral administration. A separate IRT analysis was carried out using the bridge data from the 1985-86 assessment and data from the NAEP science assessments in 1977-78 and 1981-82. The pool of items used for this scaling consisted of all items given in 1985-86 and in at least one of the previous two assessments. Due to the sparsity of items within subscales, a single scale was fit to these items.

These IRT analyses were carried out in the following manner: Age samples, rather than grade/age samples, characterize the past NAEP assessments and the 1985-86 bridge sample. The majority of items given to age 13 students were also given to age 17 students. Therefore, the age 13 and age 17 samples were combined and item parameters were estimated. Because there were too few items in common with other ages, the item parameters for the age 9 sample were estimated separately. The three-parameter logistic IRT model was fit separately to data from each age group. A comparison of assessment results from the bridge sample with results from the BIB-spiral administration indicated that the trend scale could be equated to the composite science scale, thereby accounting for the effects of changes in mode of administration and definition of age. The final scale was determined by matching the mean and standard deviation on the IRT trend scale of the 1985-86 bridge sample (with the new age definition) to the mean and standard deviation on the composite science scale of the corresponding age sample within the 1985-86 grade/age sample.

Comparison Between Mean Percent Correct and IRT Scaling

The data shown in TABLE A.6, comparing the previously reported mean percent correct for items included in the 1977 and 1982 assessments with the newly scaled science analysis for these assessments, show that the overall trend results from 1977 to 1982 using the mean proficiency values are quite similar to those using the mean percent correct statistics.

Scale Anchoring

One of NAEP's major goals has always been to describe what students know and can do and stimulate debate about whether those levels of performance are satisfactory. An additional benefit of IRT methodology is that it provides for a criterion-referenced interpretation of levels on a continuum of proficiency. Although the proficiency scale ranges from 0 to 500, few students performed at the ends of the continuum. Thus, levels chosen for describing results in the report are 150, 200, 250, 300, and 350. Each level is defined by describing the types of science questions that most students attaining that proficiency level would be able to perform successfully; each is exemplified by typical benchmark

Methodological Comparison of Mean Percent Correct and IRT Mean Science Proficiency		TABLE A.6

	Assessment Years	
	1977	1982
Age 9		
Mean Percent Correct	54.1	57.3
Mean Proficiency	219.9	220.9
Age 13		
Mean Percent Correct	55.5	55.8
Mean Proficiency	247.4	250.2
Age 17		
Mean Percent Correct	71.3	69.1
Mean Proficiency	289.6	283.3

items (see Chapter 2). Data are provided that give the estimated proportion of students at each age level and subgroup that perform at or above each of the five proficiency levels.

In the scale-anchoring process, NAEP identified sets of items from the 1986 assessment that were good discriminators between proficiency levels. The guideline used to select such items was that students at any given level would have at least a 65 to 80 percent (but often higher) probability of success with these science questions, while the students at the next lower level would have a much lower probability of success using the criterion that the difference in probabilities exceeds 30 percent between adjacent levels. Science specialists examined these empirically selected item sets and used their professional judgment to characterize each proficiency level.

Extrapolating the 1970 and 1973 Mean P-value Results onto the IRT Scale

The 1970 and 1973 science assessments were not included in the scaling of NAEP trend data. However, for the nation and several reporting subgroups (e.g., male, female) at each of the three age levels, an estimate of mean science proficiency in 1970 and 1973 was computed and is included in this report.

These estimates were obtained by assuming that the relationship within a given age level between the logit of a subgroup's mean p-value (i.e., mean proportion correct) and its respective science proficiency mean was linear and that the same line held for all assessment years and for all subgroups within the age level. Under this assumption, the between-year difference of the mean proficiency values of a subgroup for a pair of assessment years is equal to a constant (B) times the between-year difference of the logits of the mean p-values of that subgroup for the same two years. For each age level, a mean p-value estimate using a common set of items was available for adjacent assessments: 1970-1973, 1973-1977, and 1977-1982. The constant B was estimated by a regression (through the origin) of the difference between proficiency means in 1978 and 1982 on the corresponding difference between the logits of the mean p-values for these two years. All subgroups in a given age were included in the regression. For example, the estimate of the 1973 proficiency mean for a subgroup was then obtained as the sum of the 1977 subgroup mean proficiency and B times the difference between the logits of the 1973 and 1977 subgroup mean p-values (for items common to 1973 and 1977). After estimating the 1973 subgroup mean proficiency, the 1970 mean proficiency for the subgroup was estimated by the 1973 mean proficiency estimate plus B times the difference between the logits of the 1970 and 1973 subgroup mean p-values (for items common to 1970 and 1973).

Estimating Variability in NAEP Measures

The standard error, computed using a jackknife replication procedure, provides an estimate of sampling reliability for NAEP measures. NAEP uses the jackknife methodology to estimate the sampling variability of all reported statistics because conventional formulas for estimating standard errors of sampling statistics are inappropriate for use with NAEP's complex sampling procedures. The standard error is composed of sampling error and other random error associated with the assessment of a specific item or set of items. Random error includes all possible non-systematic error associated with administering specific exercise items to specific students in specific situations. The estimated population mean ± 2 standard errors represents an approximate 95 percent confidence interval. It can be said with 95 percent certainty that the performance of the population of interest is within this interval. (For a complete description of the jackknife methodology, see *Implementing the New Design: The NAEP 1983-84 Technical Report*.) In computing significant differences across the three years, the alpha for each comparison was set at $.05/2 = .025$ to control the Type I error rate for the set of comparisons within a group.

NAEP Reporting Groups

NAEP does not report performance results for individual students, but rather for groups of students. In addition to national results, this report contains information about subgroups defined by region of the country, sex, race/ethnicity, and achievement quartiles. Definitions of these groups follow.

Region

The country has been divided into four regions: Northeast, Southeast, Central and West. States included in each region are shown on the following map.

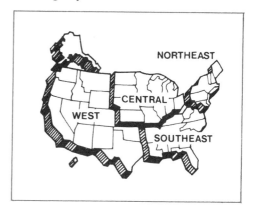

Gender

Results are reported for males and females.

Race/Ethnicity

In general, results are presented for Black, White, and Hispanic students. Following procedures used in previous assessments, trend results are based on observed racial/ethnic identifications made by assessment administrators. Grade-level results are based on student self-reports of their racial/ethnic identity according to the following categories: White, Black, Hispanic, Asian American or Pacific Islander, American Indian or Alaskan Native, and Other. The sample sizes were insufficient to permit reliable estimates for the additional subgroups defined by race/ethnicity.

Quartiles

The upper quartile presents average performance for students who were in the top 25 percent on the science proficiency scale; the lower quartile presents average performance for those in the bottom 25 percent.

Additional Background Factors

In addition to the standard NAEP reporting variables of region, gender, and race/ethnicity, and the performance quartile variable, NAEP asked all students a number of background questions. Students at grades 3 and 7 were asked about 30 questions and those at grade 11 approximately 50 questions about their school experiences and their home environment, including reading materials in the home, level of parents' education, amount of television viewing, and time spent on homework.

In addition, background questions specific to science were included in the science blocks. Students at grades 3, 7, and 11 were asked 39, 85, and 124 questions, respectively, about their course work, their attitudes toward science, and the type of instruction they had received. This report describes results for some of the individual questions asked of all students, and for several composite variables.

NAEP initiated the process of developing composite variables by conducting a factor analysis of the results to the background questions specific to science. Questions related to a given composite were identified and the Weighted Average Response Method (WARM) was then used to create the composite variable. An extension of the Average Response Method (ARM), the WARM technique is appropriate for constructing linear combinations of responses to background questions (i.e., factor scores) when not all sampled students have responded to all questions. (For further information about the ARM and WARM methods, see *Implementing the New Design: The NAEP 1983-84 Technical Report*).

THE NATION'S
REPORT
CARD

DATA APPENDIX

Mean Science Proficiency

Age 9

WEIGHTED SCIENCE PROFICIENCY MEANS
AND JACKKNIFED STANDARD ERRORS

	1976-77	1981-82	1985-86
—TOTAL—	219.9 (1.2)*	220.9 (1.8)	224.3 (1.2)
SEX			
MALE	222.1 (1.3)*	221.0 (2.3)*	227.3 (1.4)*
FEMALE	217.7 (1.2)	220.7 (2.0)	221.3 (1.4)
ETHNICITY/RACE			
WHITE	229.6 (0.9)	229.1 (1.9)	231.9 (1.2)
HISPANIC	191.9 (2.9)	189.0 (4.1)	199.4 (3.1)
BLACK	174.9 (1.9)*	187.1 (3.0)*	196.2 (1.9)*
REGION			
NORTHEAST	224.5 (1.6)	221.8 (2.7)	228.2 (3.5)
WEST	220.9 (2.3)	219.9 (4.1)	222.1 (3.2)
CENTRAL	225.3 (2.2)	226.3 (3.4)	227.9 (2.2)
SOUTHEAST	205.1 (3.0)*	214.0 (3.9)	218.8 (3.1)*
PARENTAL EDUCATION			
LESS THAN H.S.	198.5 (2.3)	198.2 (5.4)	203.6 (2.9)
GRADUATED H.S.	223.0 (1.4)	218.1 (3.2)	219.6 (1.5)
SOME EDUC AFTER H.S.	237.2 (1.5)	229.2 (3.2)	235.8 (2.6)
GRADUATED COLLEGE	232.3 (1.4)	230.6 (2.3)	235.2 (1.4)

Age 13

WEIGHTED SCIENCE PROFICIENCY MEANS
AND JACKKNIFED STANDARD ERRORS

	1976-77	1981-82	1985-86
—TOTAL—	247.4 (1.1)	250.2 (1.3)	251.4 (1.4)
SEX			
MALE	251.1 (1.3)*	255.7 (1.5)	256.1 (1.6)
FEMALE	243.8 (1.2)	245.0 (1.3)	246.9 (1.5)
ETHNICITY/RACE			
WHITE	256.1 (0.8)	257.3 (1.1)	259.2 (1.4)
HISPANIC	208.1 (2.4)*	217.2 (1.3)	221.6 (2.5)
BLACK	213.4 (2.2)	225.5 (3.9)	226.1 (3.1)
REGION			
NORTHEAST	255.3 (2.4)	254.1 (2.4)	257.6 (3.1)
WEST	243.0 (2.3)*	252.4 (3.0)	252.3 (2.7)
CENTRAL	253.8 (1.8)	253.9 (2.4)	249.4 (5.3)
SOUTHEAST	235.1 (1.8)*	238.7 (2.4)*	247.1 (2.2)
PARENTAL EDUCATION			
LESS THAN H.S.	223.5 (1.3)	225.4 (1.9)	229.4 (2.7)
GRADUATED H.S.	245.4 (1.1)	243.2 (1.3)	244.8 (1.4)
SOME EDUC AFTER H.S.	260.3 (1.2)	258.9 (1.5)	257.8 (1.4)
GRADUATED COLLEGE	266.5 (1.0)	263.5 (1.5)	264.4 (1.9)

Age 17

WEIGHTED SCIENCE PROFICIENCY MEANS
AND JACKKNIFED STANDARD ERRORS

	1976-77	1981-82	1985-86
—TOTAL—	289.6 (1.0)	283.3 (1.1)	288.5 (1.4)
SEX			
MALE	297.1 (1.2)	291.9 (1.4)	294.9 (1.9)
FEMALE	282.3 (1.1)	275.2 (1.3)	282.3 (1.5)
ETHNICITY/RACE			
WHITE	297.7 (0.7)	293.2 (1.0)*	297.5 (1.7)
HISPANIC	262.3 (2.5)	248.7 (2.4)*	259.3 (3.8)
BLACK	240.3 (1.5)*	234.8 (1.7)*	252.8 (2.9)
REGION			
NORTHEAST	296.4 (2.3)	284.4 (1.9)	292.2 (4.3)
WEST	286.6 (1.6)	280.9 (2.7)	283.2 (3.8)
CENTRAL	294.1 (1.6)	289.3 (2.4)	294.4 (2.3)
SOUTHEAST	276.4 (1.9)*	276.2 (2.8)	283.5 (2.0)
PARENTAL EDUCATION			
LESS THAN H.S.	265.4 (1.4)*	258.6 (2.3)	257.5 (3.1)
GRADUATED H.S.	284.4 (0.9)*	275.3 (1.6)	277.0 (2.0)
SOME EDUC AFTER H.S.	295.7 (1.1)	290.1 (1.7)	295.1 (2.5)
GRADUATED COLLEGE	309.3 (1.0)*	300.2 (1.7)	303.8 (2.1)

*SIGNIFICANT DIFFERENCE FROM 1986
AT THE .05 LEVEL.

Percentage of Students at or Above the Five Science Proficiency Levels

[VIRTUALLY NO 9-YEAR-OLD STUDENTS HAD SCIENCE
PROFICIENCY AT LEVEL 350.]

Knows Everyday Science Facts (150)

WEIGHTED PERCENTAGE OF 9-YEAR-OLD STUDENTS WITH SCIENCE
PROFICIENCY AT OR ABOVE 150

	1976-77	1981-82	1985-86
—TOTAL—	93.6 (0.5)*	95.0 (0.5)	96.3 (0.3)
SEX			
MALE	94.3 (0.5)*	94.0 (0.6)*	96.3 (0.4)
FEMALE	92.9 (0.6)	96.0 (0.9)	96.3 (0.4)*
ETHNICITY/RACE			
WHITE	97.8 (0.2)*	98.1 (0.4)	98.5 (0.2)*
HISPANIC	83.1 (1.6)*	84.6 (2.7)	89.6 (2.3)*
BLACK	73.1 (1.6)*	81.2 (2.0)*	87.5 (1.2)*
REGION			
NORTHEAST	94.4 (0.6)	95.4 (1.0)	96.5 (0.8)
WEST	95.2 (0.8)	94.5 (0.9)	96.5 (0.6)
CENTRAL	95.4 (0.7)	97.2 (0.9)	97.3 (0.5)
SOUTHEAST	88.0 (1.8)*	92.3 (1.3)	94.8 (1.1)
PARENTAL EDUCATION			
LESS THAN H.S.	87.0 (1.3)*	86.5 (2.7)*	94.0 (1.4)
GRADUATED H.S.	94.9 (0.5)	96.4 (0.8)	95.8 (0.6)
SOME EDUC AFTER H.S.	98.1 (0.5)	95.5 (1.3)	97.5 (0.8)
GRADUATED COLLEGE	96.6 (0.4)	97.1 (0.6)	98.1 (0.3)

Applies Basic Scientific Information (250)

WEIGHTED PERCENTAGE OF 9-YEAR-OLD STUDENTS WITH SCIENCE
PROFICIENCY AT OR ABOVE 250

	19767-77	1981-82	1985-86
—TOTAL—	26.2 (0.7)	24.8 (1.7)	27.6 (1.0)
SEX			
MALE	27.6 (0.7)	25.9 (2.3)	29.4 (1.3)
FEMALE	24.8 (0.7)	23.7 (1.8)	25.8 (1.2)
ETHNICITY/RACE			
WHITE	31.3 (0.6)	30.1 (2.0)	32.6 (1.1)
HISPANIC	3.8 (0.5)	3.8 (1.0)*	8.8 (0.9)
BLACK	8.5 (1.6)*	4.4 (2.3)	10.7 (1.9)
REGION			
NORTHEAST	29.2 (1.0)	25.7 (2.9)	31.3 (2.6)
WEST	25.6 (1.2)	22.0 (4.4)	25.8 (2.2)
CENTRAL	29.5 (1.4)	29.6 (2.6)	28.6 (1.8)
SOUTHEAST	18.3 (1.4)*	21.3 (3.4)	25.0 (2.6)
PARENTAL EDUCATION			
LESS THAN H.S.	13.6 (1.0)*	7.1 (2.2)	9.2 (1.4)
GRADUATED H.S.	27.4 (1.0)	20.7 (2.6)	24.4 (1.3)
SOME EDUC AFTER H.S.	40.2 (1.4)	35.9 (4.2)	39.2 (3.2)
GRADUATED COLLEGE	35.6 (1.0)	33.1 (2.5)	36.2 (1.2)

Understands Simple Scientific Principles (200)

WEIGHTED PERCENTAGE OF 9-YEAR-OLD STUDENTS WITH SCIENCE
PROFICIENCY AT OR ABOVE 200

	1976-77	1981-82	1985-86
—TOTAL—	67.9 (1.1)*	70.4 (1.6)	71.4 (1.0)
SEX			
MALE	69.3 (1.2)	69.3 (1.7)	72.7 (1.0)
FEMALE	66.4 (1.1)	71.6 (1.9)	70.1 (1.2)
ETHNICITY/RACE			
WHITE	76.5 (0.7)	78.0 (1.6)	78.4 (0.9)
HISPANIC	42.1 (3.1)	41.8 (5.0)	49.1 (3.3)
BLACK	27.7 (1.5)*	38.7 (2.6)	45.1 (1.9)
REGION			
NORTHEAST	72.3 (1.5)	71.8 (3.0)	75.2 (2.3)
WEST	68.5 (2.3)	70.3 (3.1)	69.1 (2.9)
CENTRAL	72.2 (2.1)	75.7 (3.0)	74.4 (2.1)
SOUTHEAST	55.0 (2.5)*	62.3 (3.8)	66.7 (2.9)
PARENTAL EDUCATION			
LESS THAN H.S.	50.1 (2.1)	51.1 (6.8)	56.3 (3.1)
GRADUATED H.S.	71.6 (1.2)	67.0 (3.6)	68.3 (1.6)
SOME EDUC AFTER H.S.	81.6 (1.2)	81.1 (2.0)	80.3 (1.8)
GRADUATED COLLEGE	77.9 (1.1)	78.4 (1.9)	80.4 (1.2)

Analyzes Scientific Procedures and Data (300)

WEIGHTED PERCENTAGE OF 9-YEAR-OLD STUDENTS WITH SCIENCE
PROFICIENCY AT OR ABOVE 300

	1976-77	1981-82	1985-86
—TOTAL—	3.5 (0.2)	2.2 (0.6)	3.4 (0.4)
SEX			
MALE	3.9 (0.3)	2.3 (1.0)	4.0 (0.6)
FEMALE	2.9 (0.2)	2.1 (0.6)	2.7 (0.4)
ETHNICITY/RACE			
WHITE	4.3 (0.2)	2.7 (0.8)	4.3 (0.5)
HISPANIC	0.5 (0.3)	0.0 (0.0)	0.2 (0.1)
BLACK	0.1 (0.1)	0.4 (0.4)	0.4 (0.2)
REGION			
NORTHEAST	3.9 (0.3)	2.1 (1.2)	5.4 (1.6)
WEST	3.4 (0.5)	2.2 (1.5)	2.8 (0.5)
CENTRAL	4.3 (0.4)	2.8 (1.5)	3.3 (0.7)
SOUTHEAST	1.8 (0.2)	1.5 (0.4)	2.4 (0.4)
PARENTAL EDUCATION			
LESS THAN H.S.	1.3 (0.3)*	0.0 (0.0)	0.4 (0.3)
GRADUATED H.S.	3.3 (0.3)*	2.9 (1.1)	1.7 (0.4)
SOME EDUC AFTER H.S.	5.4 (0.7)	2.8 (1.6)	4.4 (0.9)
GRADUATED COLLEGE	6.2 (0.4)	3.3 (1.0)	6.2 (0.7)

*SIGNIFICANT DIFFERENCE FROM 1986
AT THE .05 LEVEL.

Percentage of Students at or Above the Five Science Proficiency Levels

[VIRTUALLY ALL 13-YEAR-OLD STUDENTS HAD SCIENCE PROFICIENCY AT OR ABOVE LEVEL 150.]

Understands Simple Scientific Principles (200)

WEIGHTED PERCENTAGE OF 13-YEAR-OLD STUDENTS WITH SCIENCE PROFICIENCY AT OR ABOVE 200

	1976-77	1981-82	1985-86
—TOTAL—	85.9 (0.7)*	89.6 (0.7)	91.8 (0.9)
SEX			
MALE	87.1 (0.7)*	91.6 (0.7)	92.9 (1.0)
FEMALE	84.6 (0.8)*	87.8 (0.8)*	90.7 (0.9)
ETHNICITY/RACE			
WHITE	91.9 (0.4)*	94.5 (0.4)*	96.4 (0.7)
HISPANIC	63.1 (2.7)*	74.5 (2.6)	76.1 (3.1)
BLACK	57.1 (2.1)*	66.8 (1.6)*	74.3 (2.0)
REGION			
NORTHEAST	90.4 (1.4)	91.8 (1.1)	93.8 (1.2)
WEST	84.0 (1.4)*	90.8 (1.3)	91.0 (1.5)
CENTRAL	89.4 (1.1)	92.2 (1.1)	92.9 (3.4)
SOUTHEAST	78.0 (1.5)*	82.8 (1.8)*	89.8 (1.5)
PARENTAL EDUCATION			
LESS THAN H.S.	72.0 (1.3)	74.7 (2.3)	78.9 (3.1)
GRADUATED H.S.	86.5 (0.7)*	88.4 (0.9)*	91.1 (0.8)
SOME EDUC AFTER H.S.	93.5 (0.7)*	94.4 (0.8)*	96.6 (0.4)
GRADUATED COLLEGE	94.9 (0.4)	95.8 (0.5)	95.9 (0.5)

Analyzes Scientific Procedures and Data (300)

WEIGHTED PERCENTAGE OF 13-YEAR-OLD STUDENTS WITH SCIENCE PROFICIENCY AT OR ABOVE 300

	1976-77	1981-82	1985-86
—TOTAL—	10.9 (0.4)	9.4 (0.6)	9.4 (0.7)
SEX			
MALE	12.8 (0.6)	12.2 (0.8)	12.5 (1.0)
FEMALE	9.1 (0.4)*	6.8 (0.6)	6.4 (0.8)
ETHNICITY/RACE			
WHITE	13.1 (0.4)	11.2 (0.6)	11.8 (0.9)
HISPANIC	2.3 (0.5)	2.4 (0.7)	1.6 (0.6)
BLACK	1.2 (0.3)	0.8 (0.3)	0.9 (0.2)
REGION			
NORTHEAST	13.7 (1.0)	11.3 (1.3)	12.5 (2.0)
WEST	9.1 (0.7)	10.3 (1.5)	11.1 (1.4)
CENTRAL	12.9 (0.8)*	10.3 (1.0)	7.5 (1.3)
SOUTHEAST	7.3 (0.5)	5.2 (0.5)	6.8 (1.0)
PARENTAL EDUCATION			
LESS THAN H.S.	2.9 (0.3)	1.6 (0.5)	2.0 (0.8)
GRADUATED H.S.	8.2 (0.5)*	4.6 (0.5)	4.4 (0.8)
SOME EDUC AFTER H.S.	15.1 (0.8)*	13.3 (1.0)	9.5 (1.0)
GRADUATED COLLEGE	19.6 (0.7)	14.9 (1.0)	16.7 (1.4)

Applies Basic Scientific Information (250)

WEIGHTED PERCENTAGE OF 13-YEAR-OLD STUDENTS WITH SCIENCE PROFICIENCY AT OR ABOVE 250

	1976-77	1981-82	1985-86
—TOTAL—	49.2 (1.1)*	51.5 (1.4)	53.4 (1.4)
SEX			
MALE	52.3 (1.3)*	57.0 (1.6)	58.4 (1.9)
FEMALE	46.1 (1.0)	46.3 (1.6)	48.4 (1.4)
ETHNICITY/RACE			
WHITE	56.7 (0.9)*	58.7 (1.3)	61.9 (1.5)
HISPANIC	19.1 (1.6)	25.8 (5.0)	27.6 (3.7)
BLACK	15.1 (1.6)*	18.6 (1.4)	20.2 (2.7)
REGION			
NORTHEAST	56.0 (2.1)	54.3 (2.9)	60.5 (3.9)
WEST	45.4 (2.2)*	54.1 (3.1)	52.7 (2.7)
CENTRAL	55.5 (1.9)	55.8 (2.9)	50.8 (6.2)
SOUTHEAST	37.3 (1.4)*	40.1 (2.4)	50.4 (2.8)
PARENTAL EDUCATION			
LESS THAN H.S.	25.6 (1.1)	22.5 (1.4)	28.5 (2.7)
GRADUATED H.S.	47.3 (1.0)	44.4 (1.5)	45.4 (1.5)
SOME EDUC AFTER H.S.	60.6 (1.4)	62.6 (1.7)	62.5 (2.1)
GRADUATED COLLEGE	67.0 (1.1)	66.3 (1.7)	67.8 (1.9)

Integrates Specialized Scientific Information (350)

WEIGHTED PERCENTAGE OF 13-YEAR-OLD STUDENTS WITH SCIENCE PROFICIENCY AT OR ABOVE 350

	1976-77	1981-82	1985-86
—TOTAL—	0.7 (0.1)*	0.4 (0.1)	0.2 (0.1)
SEX			
MALE	0.9 (0.1)*	0.5 (0.2)	0.4 (0.1)
FEMALE	0.5 (0.1)*	0.2 (0.1)	0.1 (0.0)
ETHNICITY/RACE			
WHITE	0.9 (0.1)*	0.4 (0.1)	0.3 (0.1)
HISPANIC	0.2 (0.1)	0.0 (0.0)	0.0 (0.0)
BLACK	0.0 (0.0)	0.0 (0.0)	0.0 (0.0)
REGION			
NORTHEAST	1.0 (0.2)	0.4 (0.2)	0.7 (0.2)
WEST	0.5 (0.1)	0.3 (0.2)	0.2 (0.1)
CENTRAL	1.0 (0.2)*	0.5 (0.3)	0.1 (0.1)
SOUTHEAST	0.2 (0.1)*	0.1 (0.1)	0.0 (0.0)
PARENTAL EDUCATION			
LESS THAN H.S.	0.1 (0.1)	0.0 (0.0)	0.0 (0.0)
GRADUATED H.S.	0.4 (0.1)*	0.1 (0.0)*	0.0 (0.0)
SOME EDUC AFTER H.S.	0.9 (0.2)*	0.9 (0.5)	0.0 (0.1)
GRADUATED COLLEGE	1.6 (0.2)*	0.4 (0.1)	0.6 (0.2)

*SIGNIFICANT DIFFERENCE FROM 1986 AT THE .05 LEVEL.

Percentage of Students at or Above the Five Science Proficiency Levels

[VIRTUALLY ALL 17-YEAR-OLD STUDENTS HAD SCIENCE PROFICIENCY AT OR ABOVE LEVEL 150.]

Beginning Skills and Understanding (200)

WEIGHTED PERCENTAGE OF 17-YEAR-OLD STUDENTS WITH SCIENCE PROFICIENCY AT OR ABOVE 200

	1976-77	1981-82	1985-86
—TOTAL—	97.2 (0.2)	95.8 (0.4)	96.7 (0.4)
SEX			
MALE	97.9 (0.2)	96.9 (0.5)	96.9 (0.6)
FEMALE	96.6 (0.2)	94.8 (0.6)*	96.6 (0.5)
ETHNICITY/RACE			
WHITE	99.2 (0.1)	98.7 (0.2)	98.6 (0.3)
HISPANIC	92.7 (1.5)	86.1 (1.8)*	92.9 (1.7)
BLACK	84.5 (0.9)*	81.0 (1.4)*	89.8 (1.7)
REGION			
NORTHEAST	98.2 (0.4)	95.7 (0.9)	96.0 (1.2)
WEST	97.3 (0.2)	95.3 (0.8)	96.2 (0.9)
CENTRAL	98.1 (0.2)	97.4 (0.4)	98.4 (0.5)
SOUTHEAST	94.3 (0.6)	94.4 (1.3)	96.2 (0.9)
PARENTAL EDUCATION			
LESS THAN H.S.	93.6 (0.6)	91.0 (1.2)	90.8 (1.4)
GRADUATED H.S.	97.2 (0.2)	95.5 (0.6)	96.2 (0.8)
SOME EDUC AFTER H.S.	99.1 (0.1)	98.0 (0.4)	98.0 (0.7)
GRADUATED COLLEGE	99.5 (0.1)	98.3 (0.3)	99.0 (0.3)

Analyzes Scientific Procedures and Data (300)

WEIGHTED PERCENTAGE OF 17-YEAR-OLD STUDENTS WITH SCIENCE PROFICIENCY AT OR ABOVE 300

	1976-77	1981-82	1985-86
—TOTAL—	41.7 (0.8)	37.5 (0.8)*	41.4 (1.4)
SEX			
MALE	49.1 (1.0)	45.6 (1.0)	49.3 (1.8)
FEMALE	34.4 (0.9)	29.8 (1.0)*	33.8 (1.4)
ETHNICITY/RACE			
WHITE	47.4 (0.6)	44.0 (1.0)*	48.8 (1.6)
HISPANIC	19.1 (1.8)	12.5 (1.4)	15.5 (2.5)
BLACK	8.3 (0.7)	6.7 (1.1)*	12.3 (1.9)
REGION			
NORTHEAST	47.9 (1.8)	38.6 (1.3)	46.8 (3.9)
WEST	38.3 (1.4)	35.3 (2.2)	34.9 (3.4)
CENTRAL	44.9 (1.3)	42.4 (1.8)	45.7 (2.3)
SOUTHEAST	31.4 (1.8)*	32.0 (1.9)*	38.1 (1.8)
PARENTAL EDUCATION			
LESS THAN H.S.	22.0 (0.9)*	16.8 (1.4)	14.3 (2.0)
GRADUATED H.S.	35.7 (0.7)*	28.5 (0.9)	30.8 (1.5)
SOME EDUC AFTER H.S.	45.3 (1.1)	42.7 (1.4)	45.8 (2.5)
GRADUATED COLLEGE	59.4 (0.9)	53.4 (1.4)	55.3 (2.0)

Applies Basic Scientific Information (250)

WEIGHTED PERCENTAGE OF 17-YEAR-OLD STUDENTS WITH SCIENCE PROFICIENCY AT OR ABOVE 250

	1976-77	1981-82	1985-86
—TOTAL—	81.8 (0.7)	76.8 (1.0)*	80.8 (1.2)
SEX			
MALE	85.4 (0.7)	81.5 (1.1)	83.1 (1.3)
FEMALE	78.3 (0.9)*	72.4 (1.2)*	78.5 (1.5)
ETHNICITY/RACE			
WHITE	88.4 (0.4)	85.0 (0.8)	87.6 (1.4)
HISPANIC	61.7 (1.6)*	46.6 (1.8)*	61.6 (5.0)
BLACK	40.9 (1.4)*	36.5 (1.6)*	52.9 (2.7)
REGION			
NORTHEAST	85.8 (1.6)	77.4 (1.7)	81.3 (3.5)
WEST	79.9 (1.3)	75.2 (2.3)	77.8 (2.9)
CENTRAL	85.2 (1.1)	80.5 (2.0)	85.7 (1.8)
SOUTHEAST	73.0 (1.3)	72.8 (2.1)	77.6 (1.2)
PARENTAL EDUCATION			
LESS THAN H.S.	65.6 (1.2)	59.3 (1.9)	60.7 (3.2)
GRADUATED H.S.	80.1 (0.8)*	72.5 (1.4)	74.5 (1.7)
SOME EDUC AFTER H.S.	87.1 (0.8)	82.8 (1.1)	86.4 (1.8)
GRADUATED COLLEGE	93.1 (0.4)*	86.7 (1.0)	89.4 (1.4)

Integrates Specialized Scientific Information (350)

WEIGHTED PERCENTAGE OF 17-YEAR-OLD STUDENTS WITH SCIENCE PROFICIENCY AT OR ABOVE 350

	1976-77	1981-82	1985-86
—TOTAL—	8.5 (0.4)	7.2 (0.4)	7.5 (0.6)
SEX			
MALE	11.7 (0.5)	11.0 (0.6)	10.3 (1.0)
FEMALE	5.3 (0.4)	3.7 (0.3)	4.7 (0.6)
ETHNICITY/RACE			
WHITE	9.9 (0.4)	8.8 (0.5)	9.0 (0.8)
HISPANIC	2.0 (0.6)	1.4 (0.6)	0.5 (0.4)
BLACK	0.6 (0.2)	0.1 (0.1)	1.0 (0.5)
REGION			
NORTHEAST	10.7 (0.9)	7.6 (0.8)	8.9 (1.5)
WEST	6.9 (0.7)	7.0 (0.6)	6.8 (1.5)
CENTRAL	9.7 (0.5)	8.7 (0.9)	8.4 (1.5)
SOUTHEAST	5.3 (0.6)	5.0 (0.6)	5.7 (1.1)
PARENTAL EDUCATION			
LESS THAN H.S.	2.4 (0.2)*	1.2 (0.3)	0.9 (0.5)
GRADUATED H.S.	5.6 (0.3)*	3.8 (0.4)	3.7 (0.7)
SOME EDUC AFTER H.S.	8.0 (0.6)	7.8 (0.8)	7.6 (1.1)
GRADUATED COLLEGE	15.9 (0.6)*	13.0 (0.6)	12.3 (1.1)

*SIGNIFICANT DIFFERENCE FROM 1986 AT THE .05 LEVEL.

ACKNOWLEDGMENTS

This report represents the culmination of efforts by many knowledgeable individuals who generously contributed their ideas, time, and energy to the tasks of designing, conducting, and analyzing data for NAEP's 1986 science assessment. Those whose contributions were particularly significant are specifically thanked below; the help of many others whose names are not mentioned is nonetheless gratefully acknowledged.

Marion Epstein coordinated the development of the 1986 science assessment with assistance from Hessy Taft and Richard DeVore. Audrey Champagne, George Kieffer, Nuria Rodriguez, Calvin VanderWerf, and Wayne Welch were members of the Science Learning Area Committee, responsible for developing the assessment objectives. In addition, many thoughtful reviews of the objectives were contributed by teachers, school administrators, and science curriculum specialists from across the country.

Albert Beaton directs NAEP's statistical and psychometric activities. The intricate analyses described in this report were designed by Kentaro Yamamoto and Eugene Johnson, managed by Kentaro Yamamoto, and conducted by Edward Kulick, Bruce Kaplan, David Freund, Ingeborg Novatkoski, Michael Narcowich, and Alfred Rogers. Robert Mislevy designed and conducted the IRT scaling with assistance from Kathleen Sheehan, Maxine Kingston, Minhwei Wang, Jennifer Nelson, and Jo-ling Liang. John Barone directed the data analysts and provided invaluable support throughout. Bruce Kaplan, Thomas Florek, Thomas Jirele, and Ira Sample provided the graphics.

Most of the responsibility for sampling and data collection was borne by WESTAT, Inc. Norma Norris performed the statistical programming for the behavioral anchoring of the science composite. Operational aspects of the 1986 assessment were managed by Nancy Mead. Composition and printing tasks were performed by Peter Stremic.

As authors, Ina V.S. Mullis and Lynn B. Jenkins were responsible for writing this report and editing the interpretive overview. Ina Mullis, NAEP's deputy director, has been with the project since 1972 and has authored and co-authored numerous NAEP reports, including *The Reading Report Card, The Writing Report Card,* and most recently, *The Mathematics Report Card.* Lynn Jenkins, program administrator at NAEP, has extensive experience in writing and editing education research publications.

As members of the Interpretive Panel for this report, Richard Berry, Audrey Champagne, John Penick, Senta Raizen, Iris Weiss, and Wayne Welch gave invaluable assistance by contributing materials for the

150